Melanin:

A Key To Freedom

**WITH AN EXTENSIVE GLOSSARY
& BIBLIOGRAPHY**

By

RICHARD KING, M.D.

LUSHENA BOOKS, INC.

MELANIN: A KEY TO FREEDOM

First Printing :   September, 1994
Second Priting :   May, 1995
Third Printing :   October, 1998
Fourth Printing :   August, 2001

Published and Distributed By:

LUSHENA BOOKS, INC.
1804 West Irving Park Road
Chicago, IL 60613
Tel: 773-975-9945
Fax: 773-975-0045
Email: Lushena@aol.com

ISBN: 1-930097-32-8

Printed in the United States of America

DEDICATION

This book is dedicated to my children, Kent, Khadi, and Knef. This book is dedicated to you children of this next generation in the firm belief that you will stand tall upon the shoulders of your ancestors. It is written that you are the ones who will use the power of our majestic blood to reach up into the stars and hold onto it. This book is dedicated to children not yet born and generations yet to be born who may find meaning and value in the struggle of this work and their own spiral of life.

BOOKS BY THE AUTHOR

African Origin of Biological Psychiatry

MELANIN: A Key to Freedom

MELANIN & RELATED BOOKS AVAILABLE

MELANIN: The Chemical Key to Black Greatness The Harmful
Effect of Toxic Drugs on Melanin Centers Within the Black
Human. By Mr. CAROL BARNES

Jazzy Melanin.
By. Mr. CAROL BARNES

Message to the Blackman In America.
By THE HONORABLE ELIJAH MUHAMMAD

Stolen Legacy: Greek Philosophy is Stolen
Egyptian Philosophy.
By GEORGE G. M. JAMES

Light From Ancient Africa.
By NA'IM AKBAR, PH.D.

The Psychology of Color & Racial Sexual Behavior.
By KENDRYCK V. C. ALLEN

Acknowledgement

The Author would like to thank the following for their spiritual, emotional and intellectual contributions, although the views expressed in this publication do not represent their own.

Bernice Ligon and Dr. Alfred Ligon
The Aquarian Spiritual Center, Los Angeles, California
My Loving Immediate Family, consisting of Wife, Paulette, Daughter, Kent, Sons, Khadi and Knef, Sisters, Melaninee and Michele, Brothers, Wayne and Ivory, Nephew, Rutledge, Cousins, Cordell, Ricky, and Renee, Father, Louis Mother, Camille, "Star Elder" Maternal Grandmother, Ivory, "Star Elder" Paternal Great Grandfather and Black Smith of Homma, Louisiana, Louis King.

Dr. John Henrik Clarke, Professor Emeritus of African and World History, Hunter College, New York, " Master Scholar" of African History currently residing in New York City, New York

Dr. Yosefben-Jochannan, Master Scholar of African History, New York and Kemit

Prof. Hunter Adams, Chicago, Illinois

Dr. Sekmet (Patricia) Newton, Newton- Thoth, Inc., Baltimore, Maryland

Kefa and Bill Jones, First World Alliance, New York City, New York

Dr. Frances Cress-Welsing, Author, "Isis Papers", Washington, D.C.

Hon. Elijah Muhammad, The Messenger, Nation of Islam, Chicago, Illinois

Min. Louis Farrakhan, Chief Minister, Nation of Islam, Chicago, *Illinois* Min. Khalid Muhammad, Nation of Islam, Phoenix, Arizona

Prof. Carol Barnes, Author, "Jazzy Melanin," Houston, Texas

Dr. Ivan Van Sertima, Rutgers University, New Brunswick, New Jersey

Prof. Runoko Rashidi, Los Angeles, California Prof. Legrand Clegg, Compton, California

Patricia and Prof. Raymond Shields, Los Angeles, California

Prof. John Turpin, Oakland, California

Dr. Charles Finch, Morehouse University, Atlanta, Georgia Dr. Carl Word, Berkeley, California

Dr. Aminifu Harvey, Washington, D.C.

Dr. Wade Nobles and Dr. Lawford Goddard The Institute for the Advanced Study of Black Family Life and Culture, Inc., Oakland, California

Dr. Nairn Akbar, Professor of Psychology and Black Studies, Florida State University, Tallahassee, Florida

Dr. Asa Hillard, Fuller E. Calloway Professor of Urban Education, Georgili State Unviersity

Dr. Maulana Karenga, Chair, Department of Black Studies, California State University, Long Beach

Prof. Nzinga Ratabishi, President, Association for the Study of Classical African Civilizations, Los Angeles, California

Prof. Larry Williams, Atlanta, Georgia

Dr. Carl Drake, San Francisco, California

Dr. Issac Slaughter, Dr. Patricia Newton, Dr. Annette Kyle-Vega, Dr. Jean Spurlock, Dr. Lloyd Elam, Dr. Harold Jordan, Dr. Annette Kyle-Vega, Dr. Bill Lawson, Dr. Billy Jones, Dr. Richard Fields, Dr. Ezra Griffith, Dr. Phyllis Harrison-Ross, Dr. Gilbert Parks, Dr. Ramona Davis, Dr. Joseph Davis, Dr. Anna Smith, Dr .Carl Bell, Dr. Walter Shervington, Dr. Michelle Clark, Dr .Rhetta Floyd, Black Psychiatrists of America, Oakland, California National Medical Association H. Khalif Khalifah, C.E.O., U.B. & U.S. Communications Systems, Inc., Author, "Words, Acts & Deeds of Khalifah: Selected Writings: 1982 to 1992

CONTENTS

7

the El Ka'aba in Mecca

Network Computers, The Holy (Whole) Black Body Melanin System (HBB)

The HBB as Melanin Harp in a Musical Choir of Dynamic Turnover, Bulkey Electromagnetic Theory of Life linked to changes in form of multicellular Morphogenesis. Melanin structural differences between eumelanin and pheomelanin in hair.

Planetary Life Form Evolution linked to Melanin trap for Atmospheric Oxygen

Thehent, Amber and Crystal. The Kemetic Nineteenth Dynasty, Tenth Division, Book of the Gates, The flesh of Re, Melanin. The use of Colore light in Healing.

Evolution Racial/Cultural differences in the lymphatic circulation of Melanin Blood Bourne Motile Melanin Computers.

Patters of Female and Male styles of Conciousness in Relationship to the Melanin Glandular (Door, HBB, MELANIN HARP, MELANIN CHOIR OF DYNAMIC TURNOVER) Tree Translation of LIght into Ovum/Sperm (Self Replication) and or Sensory Organ Transformation (Self Replication)

INTRODUCTION

The study of Melanin is indeed an incredibly vast subject area that is the current focus of intense scientific study. This is only a brief and partial consideration of an ocean of both old and new knowledge. Please consider this study of Melanin to be but an introduction, one grain of sand on one beach of knowledge that is composed of many different sandy shorelines that all border on the same vast ocean of" Melanin Mediated Life." A future proper consideration of the subject of Melanin will address the major broad sub sections of the "Melanin Life Ocean" in the forms of (1) Cosmic Melanin (Melanin Complex Organic Molecules in Interstellar Gas Clouds in Galaxy Central Disc Regions), (2) Planetary Melanin, (3) Plant Kingdom Melanin (Chlorophyll Photopigment Equivalents), and (4) Animal Kingdom Melanin. Accordingly, this overview is focused upon just one of these four major Melanin sub sections, Animal Kingdom Melanin, particularly within the Species Homo Sapien, Humanity. Special reference is given to the epigenetic evolutionary potential within Humanity, "Son of Light," "Melanin Transformation," or "Homo Maximus" stage of Humanity.

The mind set of the student is critical to all work performed by him or her in their process of unfolding scientific observations. Every step of the scientific method is profoundly colored or better yet unconsciously projected onto-the formulation of the initial question or hypothesis to be examined, observation of various facets of the hypothesis, measurement of observed facets, analysis of facets measurement derived data, and the formulation of a final hypothesis that attempts to explain patterns of measured relationships observed between various facets of a question under observation. It is a given that in the pursuit of each step of the scientific method the process of human concentration of attention is indeed an intense process that draws upon many levels of the human experience of consciousness. Sadly, the majority of the levels of consciousness so utilized are unconscious to some scientists and their public audience.

Thus, if one is to seriously consider the current controversy existing in the 1990's over the study of Melanin despite the existence t)f ages of old and new knowledge of Melanin then be certain that this is all but testimony to the Great Need for future Melanin study.

Humanity is in desperate need of a full public uncensored study of the evolution of the Melanin mediated consciousness of Humanity over the ages and in other Animal Kingdom Life forms on this planet Earth. I am certain that this "New Age Melanin Research" will be done by those of our children who will choose life rather than witness the extinction of all Humanity.

After the readers' review of this Introduction to Melanin perhaps many readers will find themselves wondering if all of this reported Melanin research is real. Melanin research obviously defines just how essential Melanin is for Life to exist in biological systems and in Humans. Why has Melanin not become widely known in the general public? The reader may also question the validity of assuming Black to be related to inferiority or low intelligence/creativity if Melanin is shown to be critical to higher level brain function. How can White Supremacy be valid if despite differences in skin color all humans have massive amounts of Black Melanin in internal organ sites, particularly the Brain? Despite the African adaptation and survival in many harsh environment, such as the Glacial ecosystems, internally all Humanity is still quite Black on the inside.

Does not this Melanin research reveal that Humanity is a Black Africoid derived population who range in external skin color from Purple Black to White but who are all Black in the inside? Does not the past 500 year history of this planet Earth bear witness to a White Consciousness perpetuator of the greatest Human Beastly Crimes in the history of the planet Earth with a brutal European extermination of over One Billion African humans, destruction of multiple African High cultures in Africa, African terror, rape and mutilation during a slavery enforced pillage of the African Homeland Does not the past 6,000 years history of this planet earth witness a White consciousness of destruction of other vast millions of people of color ii. the continents of Europe (West Asia), Asia (East Asia), Australia, North and South America, and Africa? Was not this white consciousness expressed by some "different kind of African ", the

11

actual murders of their own African parents? Did not the past 6,000 year human history demonstrate there are indeed different styles or types of human consciousness which have been profoundly influenced by skin color and patterns of environmental lighting? What is Black Consciousness? What is White Consciousness? What is the relationship between White Consciousness, Racism, and White Supremacy? Given that we are all Africans and internally Black does a racist's distortion of biological blackness represent the work of a "sick person", a mentally ill person with a wounded Eye of Inner Vision? Is a Racist, the Original Mental Slave, Profoundly depressed and Psychotic (visual hallucination and delusional thoughts that are not based upon reality)?

Is it not true that the prison population of the United States has tripled in the past ten years? Is it not true that the current political process and electorate support further massive increases in the prison population ? Are not 45% of the prison population and the majority of death row inmates Black Males? Is not the United States for the average Black citizen already a police state with the highest rate of citizens in prison than any other nation on this planet earth? Did this county not go through a civil war over the issue of physical slavery of Black People? Was not European Industralization finaced by the African slave trade? Was not the African slave trade a triangular drug trade that involved the drugs alcohol, rum, with later expansion into opium/heroin and cocaine? Are not the same electorate and general public the real victims of blatant miseduation, horribly low standards of education and unavailable adequate mental health services? Is mental illness rampant and untreated? Are not the prisons and the schools full of underdeveloped, miseducated, misdiagnosed, ill, but latent creative geniuses? Why has Melanin research been suppressed? Why is there such a shocking ignorance of the biomedical importance of biological Blackness?

Racism is a Bad Disease, the most Prevalent Disease in the World. Racism is a Cancer of the Mind and Soul. Racism Results in Ignorance of the Body, Mind, Soul, Spirit and is Fatal. Racism is the Leading Cause of Death in the World. The Disease Racism Breeds Ignorance, the Major Diagnostic Symptoms Being Fear, Unhappiness, Depression and Psychosis.

So Be It. Racism and White Supremacy is the low ground. True Blackness, especially Melanin is by most reports Divine, the Most High Ground. Yes, BLACK MELANIN is the High Ground, the Point of Reference Upon Which This Introductionary Overview Of Melanin is Founded. The Purpose of this Introduction to Melanin is to Study the Hypothesis that Melanin is the Chemical of Life. The Evolutionary History, Life Form Embryological History, Life Form Developmental History, and particulary the Life Form PsychoSexualSpiritual Developmental History when studied have all been found to be mediated by Melanin and Melanin related Chemical/Physical Events.

The Hypothesis, Melanin is the Chemical of Life, is crucial in offering a quantifiable approach that directly leads to the study of the role of Melanin in the Process of Soul Salvation, the Freeing up, Ascension, Transformation of a Life Form into a more Conscious Type that is thereby able to attain harmonic resonance with higher levels (extremely short wavelength) of Light Radiation that prevade the Environment. This Latent Potentiality, The Soul, is freed from a robotic fear based type of consciousness that is primarily concerned with immediate survival and immediate pleasure.

To the degree that body centered ego level of consciousness persists, despite the catacylismic quakes and shakes of the body entombed soul, Optimal Health is avoided and Illness prevails in a myraid of "Soul Wake Up Calls". Racism by this definition is a form of Arrested Development in which a life form is "Frozen" or "Fixed" in a consciousness that clings to the appearance of the Body image of his/her own form and avoids visualization of the genetic memories of past parental life forms and visons of the forms of future children. The Frozen, Ego based, "Big Head", Megalomanic state of Racism exists as defensive posture to avoid poorly intergrated "Post-Traumatic Stress tagged" genetic emotional memories of Climatic/ Geological Catastrophies experienced by ancestors. In the process of adaptation by skin depigmentation, pineal calcification, lowered serum vitamin D did allow survivial of "Hypopigmented" Skin Melanin life Forms in a Glacial Climatic Geological ecosystem.

A Racist mentality will attempt to Supress (White Supremacy) the Melanin mediated Stressful "Soul Wake Up Calls"

13

that appear on a Planetary and Individual Human level. The racist will attempt to control their environment with a prolific propaganda (White Supremacy) whose central theme is that Humanity's nature is that of a Beast (Black is the sign of the devil, dirt, the "beast animal"), the universe is but one giant Heartlesss Machine (The Computer Machine is God, the highest form of human thought is male abstract strictly logical analysis) (Emotions are a sign or weakness, the undeveloped, the feminine primitive"), and thus the only sane goal, purpose, or meaning to life is to be found in the sturation of sensory experiences for immediate pleasure/pain fulfillment (Money, Money, Money, Sex, Food, Big House, Big Car).

Despite the continued rumblings and shakes of a soul so entombed in the body in such a total UNBALANCED PURSUITS OF PLEASURE, despite the endurance of a life-time of triviality and great personal sacrifices of the flesh in hope of a blissful heaven in some Heavenly after death life, despite the endless search for a "New and Better Thrill" many report that they still "hurt inside" and fell "hungry and starved inside", certainly ill.

The knowledge of what stirs to be born within the adult life form has been suppressed so long that it has actually been lost. For even the wardens of the prisons are ill and in search of this very important "lost thing", The Soul. The study of the subject of the soul has been publically labeled by some as "off limits", "pseudo-science", beyond quantifiable institutional control by numerous distorted theories which are but philosophical/religious doctrine "blind alley mind maps" that are not based upon a study of nature. The racist will attempt to hide an distort a partially lost but partially known studies of the Soul Development in Psychiatry, History, Biology, Chemistry, Physics, and Mathematics. The racist will focus upon just those segments of the scientific diciplines that only define the Ego. Nevertheless, it is this study of the role of Melanin in soul development which is supported by an expanding knowledge base-world wide works of excellent female and male scientists in .the various Colleges of the University of Nature. Humanity is now rapidly approaching the point where we will collectively recover that which has been lost, the precise mind maps for personal transformation, family relationships, and social transformations that promote Soul Salvation and Soul Development.

14

Melanin, by the nature of its vast presence in nature and frequent overlapping of Melanin-related systems and functions requires a multidisciplinary team study. Within the team approach it is of the upmost importance that an African-Centric Historical perspective be the anchor and pivot point from which such studies are conducted. This is a critical perspecive that promotes the uncovering of ancient models of Melanin research, Black Symbolism, and Psychiatry that were conducted by ancient African University scholars during a time well before the emergence of the European Racism and White Supremacy. Racism has produced widespread misinterpertation, fragmentation, suppression and loss of critical ancient African discoveries of Melanin.

This introduction will briefly review findings that point to the existence of Melanin Research and Psychological studies by Ancient Africans in Kemit. These African scholars appear to have discovered the critical psychological fact that the visualization of Black Symbols by the human mind/soul could induce dramatic shifts in states of consciousness and induce health or wounding of the Eye of Inner Vision, The Eye of Heru, The Pineal Gland. The Pineal Gland is now known during night to release into the blood/C.S.F. the hormone Melatonin. Melatonin affects the Whole Black Body Melanin System (HBB) by increasing the amount released of Pituitary M.S.H. (melanocyte stimulating hormone) thereby increasing Melanin production by skin Melanocytes which in turn directly affects Melanin production in internal organ sites.

Please consider, section 157 of the Ancient Kemetic Coffin Texts (2100-1675 B.C.E) (R.O. Faulkner, translater)," It so happened that Re said to Horns: 'Let me see your Eye since this has happened to it'. He looked at it and said: 'Look at that (black) stroke with your hand covering up the sound Eye which is there. Horns looked at that stroke and said: 'Behold, I am seeing it as altogether white'. And that is how the oryx came into being. And Re said: Look again at yonder black pig'. And Horus looked at this black pig, and Horns cried out because of the condition of his injured Eye', saying: 'Behold my Eye is like that first wound which Seth inflicted on my Eye', and Horns became unconscious in his presence. And Re said: 'The pig is detestable to Horns'."

15

Thus, over 4,000 years before the rediscovery of the unconscious and dream analysis by the psychiatrist and physician, Sigmund Freud (student and collector of Kemetic psychosymbolism), these ancient Africans were quite familiar with the concept of the unconscious and the psychological process of projection. Furthermore, they appear to have been familiar with the concepts of Inner Vision, the Eye of Hero (Pineal Gland), and endocrine relationships to visualization of Black Symbolism. These are subjects which have been lost and only partially regained by modern science.

Ancient Africans of Kemet so valued their Black Skin that there was a prohibition against altering African skin as was recorded in the 32nd of 42 Negative Confessions. Skin Melanin was directly identified under the Kemetic titles of Flesh of Ra and Flesh of Hero. Melanin or better yet Khem, the Kemetic name for Black. was seen as having "magical" properties under the name Jet (Christ). Black, a name given to the Black Ore that resulted from the Kemetic metalurgical process of separating Gold and Silver from raw Earth by the use of Mercury. On a symbolic level this process was rediscovered by the psychiatrist and physician C. G. Iung as the Symbolic Process of Alchemy, an experience in which just the process of intense concentration of attention (meditation) by the observer was seen to produce a spontaneous projection of the observer's own unconscious contents onto the subject being visualized. Symbolically, the mind (mercury) separated the Gold (Light, Astronomical effects) from the Silver (Genetic Memory, Planetary/Material Body).

Thus, it is from an African-Centric historical perspective of our African Ancestors that I have been blessed to find the Roots of this Great Melanin Black Tree of Life upon which has Blossomed a Fruit of Sacrifice, An Introduction To The Study of Melanin, Jet, Khem, The Flesh of Ra, The 1-33 Flesh of Horns, and Wosir (Osiris), The Perfect Black.

OVERVIEW OF THE CURRENT STATUS OF MELANIN RESEARCH

The study of Melanin in the human form and throughout nature is a precious key that will unlock the chains of mental slavery that presently imprison the minds of African people throughout the world. Despite the current small dance to the tunes of intentional use of miseducation, massive destruction of ancient African university libraries, scientific multimedia brainwashing propaganda, unconscious distortion of inner vision Black Symbolism, and beastly nutritional practices that produce chronic states of illness with fragmented and poorly developed inner visualization, nature's own records of Black Melanin remain quite intact and in step to a vast and far greater cosmic tune. Africans survived the horrors of hell itself, be it the countless bloody scars of physical slavery or piercing screams of the soul of mental slave, primarily because of their deeply rooted sense of spirituality. This was with experiences of the spirit, far beyond the politics of religion. African Spirituality far from being a spacey, flighty, or vague phrase is a palpable, vibrant life force that is real and can be measured by many physical scientific standards. Melanin itself on a philosophical plane is a Black chemical/biological door through which the life force of African Spirituality passes in moving from the spirit realm into the material realm. The physical identification of the Melanin Black chemical/biological door in humans is presently the subject of intense study by many laboratories throughout the world utilizing a wide array of advanced tools of science.

Yet, this is old news, a rediscovery of an old African science practiced by Af'ricans who were **FREE TO USE THEIR WILL TO DO THE WORK** to shape their world into the actual forms seen in their dreams. The dreams of inner vision were known by these angelic African ancestors to be inner vision images of heaven as seen by their own souls. For these Great and Golden dreams of the Africans were known by them to serve as a Great Compass and a Great Tuning Fork of African Spirituality, a measure (Black Nilometic Cubit Yardstick) of being at rhythm with nature and in tune with heaven itself. Melanin can he measured. African Spirituality can be measured. African life is known by Africans to be a dance to

17

music. Can you feel it? Can you let go of it? Will it let go of you? From a work which reviewed the earlier works of many great It, Part I which is available in audiotapes (1,2), videotapes (2-6), and written forms (7-17) are found these various references to the ancient African use of symbols, "Black was used extensively by ancient Africans to represent a host of concepts, all of them having in common the idea of seed, and doorway to the collective unconscious mind including; the Egyptian hieroglyph for the Egyptian God Ra, the Sun, or Horns risen (Budge 1969; Churchward, 1978) the result of the synthesis of the male principles (logical, left brain) and female principles (emotitmal, right brain); the African's great lakes Holy Land "Khui Land," birth place of humanity and home of the Twa (Annu) people (King, 1978); North pole star and seven glorious ones of the Pleaides system; Star at the summit of the cone; the all seeing eye of Horus (Churchward, 1978), representative of the god like powers of inner vision, developed in the highest grade of the African University, Sons of Light (Osiris, Perfect Black, Angel, Jet Black, Superconscious, Christ level) (James, 1976). All black strul.1ures are used with the same symbolic meaning of hidden doorway to the collective unconscious. For instance the Black stone of the Ka'ha of Mecca; Black stone Pessinus, stolen from Hannibal's city of Carthage to Rome in the last Punic War; all Black Pyramidion; the black capstone usually found at the apex of pyramids, which were themselves symbolic of the mind, Ptah, and the hill that arose from Nun, Water, Chaos (conscious awareness, doorway to the Collective unconscious); The internal structures of the Great Pyramid of Khufu being symbolic of the all black world of Amenta (Massey, 1973; Churchward, 1978). The upper most chamber of the great Pyramid, the King's chamber is an all black room symbolizing inner vision, the all seeing eye Horus, Black Dot doorway to the collective unconscious (King, 1979; Jochonnan, 1980). Concerning the Black cubit, Kamel Oshman Galet Pasha wrote in, The Nilometic Cubit, the Bulletin de la Societe Royale de Geographic Vol. 21, (1943) "The Black 1."Ubit of Ancient Egypt was of unknown origin. This cubit was carved on the Socle of the black granite colossus to the east of the entrance leading from the court of Ramses to the great colonnade, and is found only black stones or what corresponds to their symbol. Its measured length is 54l.m. R. A. Schawaller de Lubicz (1977) recently remeasured the black cubit and found its mathematical length to be 54.02376 cm."

One of the seven orders of the ancient African Egyptian educational system was that of Melanophoros, which according to Brnnson (18), "was versed in the death and immortality rites of the soul or Mystery of Osiris." Whereas according to Emboden (19) the biochemistry of both Nymphae caerulea, the sacred blue water lily (black lily) and Mandragora officinarum reveals chemicals that facilitate shamanistic trance ...sleep is the symbolic death that permits miraculous resurrection. ..The basic premise in shamanistic practices is that there is a trance in which an elect cast may communicate with deities of other worlds ...Water lily and mandrake symbolism began in the Fifth Dynasty and continued until the Ptolemaic Period. ..This cult (higher strata of priests) developed the concept of the creation of order out of chaos (Nun) in which the dark pool of nothingness gave rise to a blue water lily from which the first being arose. In most depictions the persona is that of Osiris (earlier it was Ra) ...Nymphae caerulea blooms for three consecutive days, with its blue flowers lifted 18 inches above the water on peduncles. Each day it opens at about 8:00 a.m. and closes at noon, in the full glory of Ra, the sun. At the end of the third day, the peduncle begins to twist and draw the closed flower beneath the surface of the still water where it will reach fruition. ..Three days were of extreme importance to the ancient Egyptians. ..in the combination of Osiris-Horus- Pharaoh (goal, ideal type for each citizen)."

Thus, one should not be surprised to see the same themes upon review of modem scientific literature on the subject of Black chemical/biological Melanin. The work, Black Dot, Part IV (1,3,16) contain the statements, "Melanin is a profound chemical biopolymer that is the skin color found in all racial cultural groups of humanity that range from Black through Brown to White. Melanin is produced inside a cell within the human body known as the Melanocyte, was reported by Breathnach to arise from three sources-the neural crest, optic cup, and neural tube. The neural crest is an outer layer surrounding the neural tube. The neural tube is formed in the very early embryo by a invagination or inward movement of a point (Black Dot) as a line of cells from the surface of a melanin containing ectoderm (outer layer of the gastrula stage). This rapidly multiplying ball of cells of life is the direct result of fertilization of the melanin containing female egg by the melanin containing male spermatozoa. The optic cup in the early embryo will later develop into the eye, it is from the outer wall of the optic cup that there is another site of melanocyte origin. This layer becomes the retina in all vertebrate animals and all humans regardless of the color of skin. For without a melanin black pigment layer of the retina such an eye will be blind and nonfunctional. The cranial neural tube, the result of the invagination of the melanin containing ectoderm, is the site of origin of many pigmented neurons that are found throughout the brain. The melanin found in these neurons is known as neuromelanin and is present in the brains of all humans regardless of the degree of skin color .

Furthermore, Breathnach is of the opinion that a study of melanin in body sites other than the skin or eye (a site such as the inner ear) reveals melanin's role in a redox capacity, electron transfer agent, amorphous semiconductor threshold switch, electron-photon coupler, accumulator of drugs and metal ions, and has cationic exchange properties. ..In a sense, and certainly from the point of view of developmental lineage, the pigment cells could be regarded as highly specialized neurons, just as the photoreceptors are. ..we should think more of probable "neuronal" functions and activity of the pigment cells. ..Consideration of the general biophysical and biochemical properties of melanin has further led to speculation that in the ear, it may serve as a reservoir for trace elements, a sink for free radical species."

Evidence of the current intense world wide study of Melanin can be easily appreciated upon reviewing the many publications by Afrocentric authors such as King (1-17), Barnes (20), Welsing (21); new theorists such as Barr (22), Breathnach (23),and Meyer zum Gottesberge (25); and a vast host of other researchers who comprise the International Pigment Cell Conference (26) members with the three regional societies of the Pan American Society for Pigment Cell Research, and the Japanese Society for Pigment Cell Research. The International Pigment Conferences has held fifteen International Pigment Cell Conferences (1,16) since 1946, the last being held in London in 1993. Whereas, Afrocentric scholars in the study of Melanin have held seven International Melanin conferences through the KM-WR Science Consortium, Inc. all in the United States.

REFERENCES

Audiotapes-90 Minute Tapes

1. Tapes-1-4, *Black Dot, Eye of the Soul,* Black Dot, *Melanin,* Part I-IV; Eye of Heru, Eye of the Soul, Pineal Gland, a review of the scientific literature from 1940 through 1992, Richard D. King, M.D., 1993.
2. Tapes-1-3, *Uraeus: From Mental Slavery to Mastership Parts I-IV,; The Kemetic Images of Light,* Richard D. King, M.D., 1993. Videotapes-120 Minute Tapes.
3. Tapes-1-3, *Melanin and the Pineal Gland,* Public Lecture, Know Bookstore, Durham North Carolina 1993. A Review of the Kemetic Origins of the Study of Inner Vision and its relation ship to Melanin and the Eye of Heru, Pineal Gland, Utilizing Pineal Gland scientific literature through 1992 and Melanin scientific literature through 1993, Richard D. King, M.D.
4. Tape 1, *Melanin and Pineal,* Public Lecture, Medgar Evers College, New York, New York, 30 slides, richard D. King, M.D. 1991
5. Tape 1, *Afrocentric History, Melanin and the Pineal Gland* Long Beach, California, 100 Slides, Richard D. King, M. D. 1991
6. Tape 1, *Melanin and the Eye of Heru (Pineal Gland)* Interview of Richard D. King, M.D. by Listervelt Middleton, on the River Hapi (Nile) in Abu (Aswan), Egypt, ASCAC, 1987
7. King, Richard D., *Uraeus, From Mental Slavery to Mastership,* Parts I-IV, Uraeus, V. 1, N. 1-4, Aquarian Spiritual Center, 1342 W. M.L. King Blvd., 90037, 1978
8. King, Richard D., Black Dot, Black Seed, Part I, Uraeus, V. 2, N. 1, Aquarian Spiritual Center, 1342 W. M.L. King Blvd., 90037, 1980
9. King, Richard D., *Black Dot, The Archetype of Humanity,* Uraeus V. 2, N. 3, Aquarian Spiritual Center, 1342 W. M.L. King Blvd., 90037, 1982
10. King, Richard D., *The African Origin of Biological Psychiatry,* 1988
11. King, Richard D., *The African Origin of Biological Psychiatry,*

Seymor Smith, Germantown, Tenn. 1990

12. King, Richard D., *Select References to the Eye of Heru from the Pyramid Texts,* 1990.

13. King, Richard D., *Select References to the Eye of Heru from the Coffin Texts, 1991.*

14. King, Richard D., *Kemetic Images of Light, 1992*

15. King, Richard D., *The Pineal Gland, The Eye of Heru, 1992*

16. King, Richard D., *Melanin, Black Dot* Part IV, 1993

17. King, Richard D., *Black Symbolism of the Unconscious:* Part 1, A Review of Black Symbolism in the Collected Works of C.G. Jung, 1, 1993

18. Brunson, James E., *Frat and Soror, The African Origin of Greek Lettered Organizations,* A Cleague Group Publication, p. 89, 1991

19. Emboden, William, *The Sacred Journey in Dynastic Egypt: Shamanistic Trance in the Context of the Narcotic Water Lily and the Mandrake,* J. of Psychoactive Drugs, V. 21, N. 1, p. 61-75, 1989

20. Barnes, Carol, Melanin: *The Chemical Key to Black Greatness, The Harmful Effect of Toxic Drugs on Melanin Centers Within the Black Human,* C.B. Publishers, Houston, Texas, 1988

21. Welsing, Frances Cress, *The Cress Theory of Color Confrontation and Racism* (White Racism), Washington, DC.,C.R. Publisher, 1970

22. Barr, Frank, *Melanin: The Organizing Molecule, Medical Hypothesis* 11, p. 1-140, 1988.

24. Meyer zum Gottesberge, A.M., *Phsiology and Pathophsiology of Inner Ear Melanin,* Pigment Cell Research, V. 1, P. 238-249, 1988

25. MIshima, Yutaka, *Preface to the Proceedings of the 14th International Pigment Cell Conference,* Kiobi, Japan, 1990, Pigment Cell Research Supp., V. 2, p. xv, 1992

MELANIN AND THE BRAIN, NEUROMELANIN, 12 BRAIN STEM PIGMENTED NUCLEII

Within the human brain stem are twelve centers of black melanin. These twelve centers are the (1) locus coeruleus, (2) substantia nigra, (3) brachialis, (4) paranigralis, (5) intracapularis subcerleus, (6) nervi trigeini, (7) mesencepahsius, (8) pontis centralis oratis, (9) tegmenti pedennculopontis, (10) parabrachialis, (11) medialis dorsomotor, and (12) retro ambilgualis. All animal life with a spinal column, vertebrates, have varying degrees of melanin pigmentation of these twelve centers. The earlier life forms such as fish, amphibians, and reptiles have fewer of the twelve centers to be pigmented. Whereas the phylogentically advanced life forms have more of the centers pigmented with mammals having the largest number of pigmented brain melanin (centers). Of all primates it is the near human type chimpanzee that has eleven of the twelve centers to contain deep black melanin pigmentation.

Critically, only humans have deep melanin pigmentation of all twelve brain centers. The one brain center deeply pigmented with black melanin only in humans but not other primates or other animal forms is known as the **Locus Coeruleus**. The Locus Coerueleus literally means, **Black Dot**. Locus is a latin word, stlocus locum, meaning point or dot. Coeruleus is a Sanskrit word, caerleus yamas, meaning black. The philosophical concept of the **Black Dot** is a key concept found at the core of ancient African Systems of Knowledge such as the ancient Annu hieroglyphic name for Khui Land, the Great Lakes site of the birth place of humanity and the Egyptian hieroglyphic name for sun god Ra. This is profound evidence that ancient Africans studied brain anatomy and named this brain site **Black Dot** because its appearance and function revealed evidence of a symbolism, chemistry, anatomy, and history that was in line with then known research evidence of the role of Black Melanin throughout nature.

Modern science has rediscovered some of the relationships that the Locus Coeruleus has to other brain structures. Cells of the Locus Coeruleus provide the principal noradrenergic, norepinephrine, nerve supply to many areas of the brain-cerebral cortex, hippocampus, cingulate gyrus, and amygdala areas that make up the major portion of the limbic cortex. The locus coeruleus also suplies part of the norepinephrine found in other brain areas such as hypothalamus, thalamus, pineal gland, habenula (deep pineal), cerebellum; lower brain stem and spinal cord. The Locus Coerueleus appears to be involved in memory for a malfunction of this melanin brain center can result in amnesia. The locus Coeruleus is also involved in emotions such as anxiety with a continum of cautionary or inhibitory functions by this black brain center in which the middle or normal range of function is experienced as vigilance, caution, prudence, watchfullness, and attentiveness. Whereas high coeruleus function may display feelings of terror, panic, fear, anxiety, dread, and alarm. Minimum locus coeruleus function may display feelings of inattentiveness, distractibility, impulsivity, carelessness, recklessness and fearlessness. This has major treatment implications for the illness states of mental slavery, racism, depression, anxiety, and post traumatic stress syndrome.

Last, the pineal gland, releases a hormone, Melatonin, during night that has a vast array of effects. One of the major effects is activation of the brain site, area postrema, which in turn activates the Locus Coeruleus, to induce R. E. M. sleep. R. E. M. sleep is that phase of sleep during which neophyte humans can consciously recall' their dreams of travel and communication with other internal memory pools and or external other dimensions of life in nature, Trance States.

Again, evidence of the current intense world wide study of Melanin can be easily appreciated upon reviewing the many publications by Afrocentric authors such as King (1-17), Barnes (20), Welsing (21); new theorists such as Barr (22), Breathnatch (23),and Meyer zum Gottesberge (25); and a vast host of other researchers who comprise the International Pigment Cell Conference (26) members with the three regional societies of the Pan American Society for Pigment Cell Research, and the Japanese Society for Pigment Cell Research. The International Pigment Conferences has held fifteen International Pigment Cell Conferences (1,16) since 1946, the last being held in London in 1993. Whereas, Afrocentric scholars in the study of Melanin have held seven International Melanin conferences through the KM-WR Science Consortium, Inc. all in the United States.

MELANIN AND THE EYE

Black Melanin is a critical biopigment for vision in the eyes of humans and all life forms with a spinal column, vertebrates. The inner lining of our two lateral eyes contain the retina, a structure with both rods and cones. Rods are sensory organ receptors that produce black and white vision by capturing particles of light, photons, when light passes through the pupil to reach the inner retinal lining of the eye. The rod photopigment, rhodopsin, upon capturing light changes shape from a cis (chair shape) into a trans (boat shape), thereby holding onto the light photon, the rhodopsin containing disc is then shed, falling into the deeper melanin pigment layer of the retina. In the pigmented layer of the retina the light photon is transferred into the Melanin molecule which in turn transforms the photon into an electrical-chemical message that passes into the optic nerve and then the optical nerve tracts into other parts of the brain for processing. Color vision is produced by the retina by Melanin through a similar process by utilizing other photopigments in a different receptor type, the cones. **Without the melanin In the pigmented layer of the retina a life form will be permanently blind, Light vision Is born from Blackness, Melanin** -(Creel, D., O'Donnell, F. E., Visual System Anomalies in Human Ocular Albinos, Science, 201, p. 1253,1980; Path, M. O., Phagocytosis of Light and Dark-Adapted Rod Outer Segments by Cultured Pigment Epithelium, Seicne, 203, p. 526,1978)

Another critical reference to the role of Melanin in visual systems is found in the scientific report, Drager, U. C., Albinism and Visual Pathways, The New England Journal of Medicine, V. 314, N. 25, p. 636, 1986. This scientist reported, "Oculocutaneous albinism is an autosomal recessive disorder that is distinguished by uniform hypopigmentation of the skin, hair, and eyes. Involvement limited to the eyes (ocular albinism) has also been described. Because a lack of melanin pigment results in reduced photoreception of the skin, carcinomas (cancer) may develop in exposed areas. A similar loss of photoreception in the eyes lead to photophobia (fear and avoidance of light). Less often appreciated, however, are more complex disturbances of the visual system, which are common in albinism and other conditions characterized by hypopigmetation." In hypopigmented humans a misrouting of the optic tract nerves results in a lack of binocular vision and optokinetic nystagmus (constant fluttering movement of the eyes in a horizontal or vertical direction). Drager was of the opinion that optokinetic nystagmus as a defect was caused by, "a miswiring at the level of the retina in such a way that phyisologic property of some cells-their directional selectivity- is inverted by 180 degrees." A fourth defect is night blindness, a condition that occurs in hypopigmented vertebrate life forms, elevated recorded visual thresholds resulting from the influence upon photoreceptor function.

Drager reported, " In mice, more than 60 genetic loci with about 170 mutations are known to affect pigmentation. Most of these genes probably have homologues in the human genome, but only some of these will be apparent as pigment mutations. Only one of the pigmentation loci-the albino Locus-codes for the enzyme specifically involved in melanin synthesis, and the enzyme has no other known functions.. ..What is the function of the large number of pigmentation genes that do not code for tyrosinase? In practically no case is the answer known in terms of coded protein, but a bewildering list of pleotrophic effects indicates that the pigmentation system shares cell biologic functions with many other systems. ..The retinal pigment epithelium, which is derived from the optic up (part of the neural tube), becomes pigmented at an early crucial stage of eye development, when specification events are thought to take place that determine coordinates of the retina and its decussation pattern for life. In humans this occurs about eight months before birth. The synthesis of melanin at this stage seems to influence the establishment of the visual plan even before there are any visual connections."

MELANIN AND THE EAR

Black Melanin is a critical biogpigment, The Black Chemical of Life, found throughout the entire body of all humans, skin, eyes, brain, endocrine glands, blood, heart, lungs, gastrointestinal tract, kidney/urogential tract, sexual organs, et. Of course melanin is also present in the ear of humans and is critically involved in the hearing of sound. Perhaps, given the current phase of world wide high achievements by the creative talents of Africans in the arena of music the study of melanin, hearing, and music, may be a "key to the key" of melanin as a key to freedom. The study of sound is a study of vibration and music (harmonics/resonance=key). Sound is a form of light, particular range of vibrations or movements of atoms in the spectrum of light, Life. Melanin as a photoreceptor, receiver of light, is a door through which light enters the human form through the various sensory organ information portals to self organize, to feed the self or soul of humans while in the physical body.

Melanin is found throughout the ear in humans and the presence of melanin in the inner ear is of great importance. Marie-Louise Barrenas and Fredrik Lindgren in their article, The Influence of Inner Ear Melanin On Susceptibility To TTS In Humans, Scan. Audiol. 199019:97-102 reported, "In the literature most reports concerning thresholds or permanent NIHL (PTS) (ABILITY TO HEAR SOUND) in different ethnic groups or races indicate that hearing is better preserved in coloured than in white populations. Buch & Raiford (1931) studied the hearing function in colored and white American hospital patients with the same cultural background and found that the hearing thresholds were superior in coloured compared with white males in the frequency range above 2kHz, and this difference increased with age. Roset et. al. (1962) investigated hearing thresholds in 541 primitive tribes people living in a relatively noise-free area in the Republic of Sudan. These people showed better hearing threshelds in the high frequencies than has been reported from any similar study of modem western civilization. Post (1964) evaluated the results of hearing examinations of American conscripts from World War II and found that coloured men above middle age had better hearing thresholds at high frequencies than white men in the same age groups, especially in males over 30 years of age. Karsai et. al. (1972) studied 836 dock workers with relatively uniform background of noise exposure and found significantly better hearing thresholds for high frequency tones among coloured workers than among white workers. Royster et. al. (1980) investigated a noise-exposed population and found that black females as a group tended to show less loss at higher ages than did the white males.

In 1985, Attias & Pratt (Auditory-Evoked Potential Correlates of Susceptibility To Noise-Induced Hearing Loss. Audiology 1985: 24:149-56) found significant correlation between iris and skin pigmentation on the one hand and susceptibility to noise on the other, i. e., the more pigment in the iris (outer surface of eye) and skin, the less PTS (low susceptibility). ..Tota & Bocci (1967) (The Importance Of The Colour Of The Iris On The Evaluation Of Resistance To Auditory Fatigue. Rev. Otoneuroophtalmol 42: 183-92) and Hood et. al. (1976) (The Influence Of Eye Colour Upon Temporary Threshold Shift. Audiology 15:449-464) found a positive correlation between eye-color and TTS, i. e., brown-eyed persons were less suspectible to TTS than blue- eyed persons.

Thus, melanin is critical to hearing. African people hear a wider range of sound than Europeans in particular the low bass sounds. Indeed, the "Blacker The Berry The Sweeter The Juice," -the Blacker the color of the Eye (Iris) there is more melanin (Juice of Life) present in the inner ear and the greater the ability to hear sound/light. This universal law concerns the role of melanin as an energy translational door that applies to most sensory organ receptors be it skin (feeling/touch/gravity), eye (vision), hearing (sound), taste, and smell and their corresponding soul extrasensory expansions. (Ernest J. Stevens, Lights, Colors, Tones and Nature's Finer Forces: Marvelous Discoveries, Basic and Active Principles, Functions of Electrons, Magnetons, Atoms, Cold-Lights, Odics, Auras and Radio 1974 Health Research P. 0. Box 70 Mokelumne Hill, California 95245) (Arthur M. Young The Reflexive Universe: Evolution of Consciousness, 1976, Robert Briggs Associates, Box 9, Mill Valley, California 94941).

A. M. Meyer Zum Gottesberge, in the article, Physiology and Pathophysiology of Inner Ear Melanin, Pigment Cell Research 1988 1:238- 249 has written that melanin in the inner ear is involved in the control of calcium ions by the actual movement of the melanin containing cells, melanocytes along inner ear blood vessels and the inner ear endolymphatic fluid.

Again, evidence of the current intense world wide study of melanin can be appreciated upon reviewing the many publications by Africancentric such as King (1-17), Barnes (20), Welsing (21); new theorists such as Barr (22), Breathnach (23) and Meyer zum Gottesberge (25); and a vast assembly of other scientists who comprise the international Pigment Cell Conference.

MELANIN AND THE PINEAL GLAND, DEVELOPMENT OF INNER VISION

Black Melanin is a critical biopigment, The Black Chemical of Life, found throughout the entire body of all humans in their skin, eyes, brain, endocrine glands, blood, heart, muscles, lungs, gastrointestinal tract, kidney/urogenital tract, sexual organs, etc., Despite the presence of melanin in many body locations and in receptor sensory organs as a transformation door the melanins may function as a unified whole Black system. A study of ancient African history reveals that THE HUMAN MELANIN SYSTEM FUNCTIONS AS A (WHOLE) HOL Y BLACK BODY (HBB) AS THE INNER VISION EYE OF THE SOUL, TO PRODUCE TRUE SPIRITUAL CONSCIOUSNESS, CREATIVE GENIUS, BEATIFIC VISION, TO BECOME GOD-LIKE, AND TO HAVE CONVERSATION WITH THE IMMORTALS (Ancestors).

According to George E. James in the book, *Stolen Legacy,* Chapter three, p. 27 (U. B. & U. S. Communications Systems, Inc.), "The earliest theory of salvation is the Egyptian theory. The Egyptian Mystery Systems has as its most important object, the deification of man, and taught that the soul of man if liberated from its bodily fetters, could enable him to become godlike and see the Gods in this life and attain the beatific vision and hold communion with the Immortals..."The Egyptian Mystery System, like the modem University, was the centre of organized culture, and the candidates entered it as the leading source of organized culture Accoding to Pietschmann, the Egyptian Mysteries had three grades of students (1) The Mortals i. e., probationary students who were being instructed, but who had not yet experienced the inner vision. (2) The Intellegences, i. e., those who had attained inner vision, and had received mind of n011s and (3) The Creators or Sons of Light, who had become identified with or united with Light (i. e. true spiritual consciousness)."

The EYE OF INNER VISION for all humans is the EYE OF HERU (HORUS), the EYE OF THE SOUL, THIRD EYE, PINEAL GLAND, EPIPHYSIS CEREBRI. Despite a claim by Europeans that

30

Herophilos, a Greek Library of Alexandria professor in the third century B. C. was the first discoverer of the pineal gland, he was in fact a student of African Egyptian professors of Medicine. These African male and female Physicians belonged to the Pastophori Order (College) of the Egyptian University (Mystery System) which had flourished as an intact Educational Academy for over four thousands years prior to the appearance of the Greek Library and Museum in Alexandria, Egypt. These African scientists had defined in their written texts (42 Books of Tehuti, Pyramid Texts, Coffin Texts, Book of the Coming Forth By Day (Book of the Dead) the detailed location, physiology, and relationship of the Eye of Heru (Pineal Gland) to the sun light, Star light, Moon light, Soul and the Black Whole Body Melanin System.

In the middle of the first three sections of the upper register right panel of the second shrine of Pharoah Tutankhamun, Egyptian 18th Dynasty, there is a picture of star light (sun light) being directed into the human midforehead (Piankoff, Alexander, The Shrines of Tutankhamun). This is the site of the pineal gland, the only structure in the interior of the head that is sensitive to enviommentallight. This was written by Africans 1,200 years before Herophilos and 3,300 years before the rediscovery of the pineal- sunlight relationship by modem European scientists. (R. J. Reiter, The Pineal Gland, Vol. I-III, 1982). With sunlight, the pineal releases into blood the hormone serotonin. During nighttime the pineal releases into the blood melatonin, a hormone that directly effects melanin production in many sites throughout the body. (R. King, African Origins of Biological Psychiatry, p. 49).

Indeed, the Pineal Gland is the uppernlost in a chain of glands found from the crown of the head including the pituitary, with many gland" along the spinal column and of course the melanin containing melanocytes in the skin. These gland5 are part of the (Whole) Holy Black Body (HBB) and is partially known in modem science as the A.P.U.D. system (Amine Decarboxylase system). All of the glands of this system contain the A.P.U.D. enzyme that allows for special handling of carbon atoms (key Black atom of Melanin). All glands of the A. P.U.D. system originate from the brain structure, the neural crest, which develops from an invagination of the Melanin containing ectodernllayer of the skin of the early prefetus. (Pearse,

A.G.E., J. Histochem. Cytochem. 17 (5)); 303-313.

In the middle section of the same section of Pharoah Tutankhamun's shrine are six mummiform figures which have translated by Rkhty Amen- Jones (King, p. 47) -(1) Head of Horus, (2) Face of Horus, (3) Neck of Horus, (4) 133-tissue of Horus, (5) Inner? Eye, (6) Doorway. The 1-33-tissue of Horns has also been translated by Piankoff as "Fine Stuff. " Fine Stuff and the I 33-tissue of Horus may have been the ancient African scientific names for Melanin. Certainly, given Melanin's clear role as the chemical of life and a doorway through which are passed and translated the full sprectrum of wavelengths of light (life) in nature. Indeed, Melanin as a Fine Stuff is a truly typical African way of expressing such a Profound Sweet Thing. Furthermore, for the ancient Africans to name link melanin with the pineal, I, and 33 reveals an African knowledge of high science. For the capital I (soul development) results from a conversion, raising upright the 33 bone vertebral column from a horizontal dead level of the small case i (ego/lower mind, the beast), upon the freedom or salvation of the soul from the physical body by a process of education. The whole body melanin grandular system found along the 33 vertebrate spinal column increases in hormone production and electrical/magnetic glandular interrelationships during the course of this process (King, p. 93-129).

MELANIN AND THE PINEAL GLAND, BONE DENSITY RELATIONSHIPS TO SKIN MELANIN

Black Melanin is a critical biopigment, The Black Chemical of Life, found throughout the entire body of all humans in their skin, eyes, brain endocrine glands, blood, heart, muscles, lungs, gastrointestinal tract, kidney/urogenital tract, sexual organs, etc. Melanins although present in many different body locations function as a Whole Holy Black Body (HBB). The Black Dot, Eye Of Hero, Pineal Gland, Third Eye. The eye of Hero Produces True Spiritual Consciousness, Creative Genius, Beatific Vision, To Become Godlike, and to Have Conversation With the Immortal (Ancestors). Over a continuous period of four thousand years prior to the emergence of Greek Library of Alexandria there were African Physician Professors of the African Educational Academy, The Egyptian Mystery System, defined The Eye of Heru in their written texts (42 Books of Thehuti, Pyramid Texts, Texts, Coffin Texts, Book of the Coming Forth By Day (Book of the Dead). These African Female and Male Professors of the Kemetic University, The Mystery System of Kemit (Egypt) in these various written texts did define in detail the location, physiology, and relationship of the Eye of Heru (Pineal Gland) to Sun light, Moon light, Soul and the Holy Black Body (HBB). The Holy Black Body (HBB) was named by these ancient Africans as the I 33 Tissue of Horus, Fine Stuff, and Flesh of Ra.

In the middle of the first three sections of the upper register right panel of the second shrine of Pharoah Tutankhamun, Egyptian 18th Dynasty, 1530 B. C. (1,200 years before the Greek Library of Alexandria are six mummiform figures which have been translated by Rkhty Amen-Jones (R. King, The African Origin of Biological Psychiatry, p. 49,1990)-(1) Head of Horus, (2) Face of Horns, (3) Neck of Horns, (4) I 33-tissue of Horns, (5) Inner?) Eye, (6) Doorway. The I 33 Tissue of Horns has also been translated by Piankoff as "Fine Stuff" (A. Piankoff, The Shrines of Tutankhamun, Princeton Univ. Press, 1977). The concept of the Eye of Heru as an Inner Eye is self clear and self explanatory. For inner vision was a level of conscious operation, the direct use of the soul over and above the use of the mind that was developed in the African University students in grade 2, Intellegence, and grade 3, Sons of Light (George James, *Stolen Legacy,* Chapter 3). The educational system of the ancient Kamites literally increased the vibratory rate, and hormone secretion of Melatonin, a melanin activating hormone. Doorway refers to the doorway of the anterior fontanele, cranial sutures on the top of the skull, through which the soul is said to pass during the course of out of body travel. Doorway also refers to the operation and function of Melanin in each of the many locations of Melanin in the body as it is influenced by the Pineal hormone Melatonin.

The 1-33 Tissue of Hem definition of the Eye of Hero by the ancient African Physicians clearly reveals a knowledge of high science and the relationship of the Eye of Hem to the Whole Body Melanin System, The Fine Stuff. There are three glands in the neck that are controlled by the Eye of Heru Pineal Gland- Thyroid, Parathyroid, Thyrocalcitonin Cells. The parathyroid hormone produces the hormone parathyroid hormone (PTH) which pulls calcium out of bone storage to increase blood levels of calcium. Whereas Thyrocalcitonin cells increases the storage of calcium into bone from blood. Bell (N. H. Bell, Vitamin D-endocrine system. J. Clin. Invest. 76: 1-6,1985) reported that in Black people there is found a higher level of PTH hormone and fully activated vitamin D hormone (1, 25(OH) 2D than found in Whites. The Pineal Gland secretions increase the level of hormone secretions by the Parthyroid Gland, PTH (1. D. Kiss, Acta. Medica Academinae Seientiarom Hungaricae, Tomus 26 (4):363-370). The Eye of Heru/Pineal Gland secretions decrease the Thyroid and Thyrl1Calcitonin hormone secretions (G. Csaba, Acta. biol. Acad. Sci. Hung. 19 (1):35-41, 1968. Melanin is present within the pineal gland (E. Santamarina, Canad. 1. Biochem. Physiol. 36:227-235,1958) and it determines a higher level of pineal hormone secretions as found in Black people (King, 1994, W. Pelham, 1. Clin. Endocrinol. Metab. 37:341-344,
1973).

The Eye of Heru, Pineal Gland, is linked to the neck glands (Thyroid, Parathyroid, Thyrocalcitonin) and Melanins (Skin, and other Whole Body Melanin Sites) through Calcium and Vitamin D. The formation of vitamin D first begins in the skin as a previtamin 7

-dehydrocholesterol. When light passes through the skin-Melanin layer it energizes and converts into D3 which then passes into the blood, transported to the liver and converted (hydrosylation) to 25-hydroxyvitamin D (25-0HD) then passed in the blood to the kidney for final conversion (hydroxylation) to form 1,25 $(OH)_2D$, Vitamin D (T.C. Clemens, Lancet 1:74-76,1982; M.F. Holick, Science 211 (6): 590-593, 1981). Critically, this final stage of vitamin D formation is controlled by PTH which exists in a higher blood level in blacks than whites because Blacks have less pineal calcification and accordingly higher blood levels of pineal melatonin (G. M. Vaughan,J. Clin. Endocrinol. Metab. 42: 752-764) which raises the level of PTH. It is known that the color of the outer coat of the eye, iris, reflects the degree of pigmentation in internal sites such as the inner ear and by logical extension, the pineal (J. D. Hood, Audiology 15: 449-464. 1976). Thus. not only do Black people have a lower incidence of pineal calcification, higher levels of pineal secretion of melatonin, and Blacks have a 5-10% greater density of their bones, and a markedly lower rate of osteoporosis in females after menopause when compared to white females (Williams, 1990: S. Cohn, Metab. Clin. Exp. 26: 171-178, 1977). Thus, calcium, and vitamin D serve a feed back role to allow the Eye of Heru/Pineal Gland to determine the efficiency of skin melanin and other body sites of melanin role as a doorway in the reception of light.

MELANIN AND THE PINEAL GLAND, KEMETIC DEVELOPMENT OR THE PINEAL GLAND

A STUDY OF ANCIENT AFRICAN HISTORY REVEALS THE AFRICAN DEFINITION OF THE HUMAN MELANIN SYSTEM AS A HOLY BLACK BODY (HBB) THAT SERVES AS THE EYE OF THE SOUL TO PRODUCE INNER VISION, TRUE SPIRITUAL CONSCIOUSNESS, CREATIVE GENIUS, BEATIFIC VISION, TO BECOME GODLIKE, AND TO HAVE CONVERSATION WITH THE IMMORTALS (ANCESTORS). THE PURPOSE OF ANCIENT AFRICAN EDUCATION WAS TO PROVIDE THE KNOWLEDGE AND DEVELOPMENT OF THE WILL OF THE STUDENT THAT ALLOWED SALVATION (FREEDOM) OF THE SOUL FROM THE FETTERS (CHAINS) OF THE PHYSICAL BODY. (George James *Stolen Legacy),* Chapter 3, U. B. & U. S. Communications Systems) MELANIN IS THE CHEMICAL OF LIFE, THE CHEMICAL OF THE SOUL, A TRANS- PHYSICAL DOORWAY TROUGH WHICH THE ENERGY WAVES OF THE HOLY SOUL, SPIRIT, AND MIND PASS TO TAKE FORM AS THEE HOLY BLACK BODY. ANCIENT AFRICANS IN KEMIT (EGYPT) VIEWED ALL THE CONTENTS OF AMENTA (THE UNDERWORLD- PERSONAL SUBCONSCIOOUS (MIND), SUPERCONSCIOUS (SOUL), COLLECTIVE UNSCIOUS (SPIRIT) AS JET BLACK IN COLOR.

The Eye of the Soul was named the Eye of Hem in Kemit, the Eye of Inner Vision. Inner Vision of expanded use of the Eye of Hem was developed by a Kemetic System of Education (James). Students of grade 2, Intelligence, and grade 3, Sons of Light, attained Inner Vision. It appears that this form of vision resulted from a synthesis, union, or global development of the brain. The Right Cortex (emotional radar, intuitive emotions) was developed by a control of the passions and raising up of the intuitive emotions by intense study and practice of the Ten Virtues (James) and 42 Negative Confessions (Budge, W., Osiris and the Egyptian Resurrection, University Books, New Hyde Park, N. Y. pp 340,1961. The Left Cortex was developed by intense study of the laws of nature with practice of the Seven

Liberal Arts (James) thereby purging the mind of irrational tendencies and allowing the student to will one's conduct to be in rhythm with nature. When a student had become able to equally use both the left and right cerebral hemispheres of their own brain they experienced Inner Vision. African students of Grade 2, Intelligence, experienced Inner Vision through an increased activity of the Eye of Heru, the Pineal Gland. the internal midline Eye/Gland found in the middle of the brain in between the cortical hemispheres. African students of Grade 3, Sons of Light. experienced a greater level of Inner Vision that allowed an actual unity with light and the ability to have conversation with the Immortals. On this level of Inner Vision the student equally used both cortical hemispheres in a manner that unified the two cortical styles of consciousness with input from the deeper more ancient brain structures of the mid brain. brain stem, spinal column. all glands of the entire body (blood, lymph, peripheral nerves) and particularly the Whole Black Body (HBB).

Please consider the nerves that control some aspects of the Eye of Hem, the Pineal Gland. Moller has written. (Moller. M., Fine structure of the pinealopetal innervation of the mammalian pineal gland, Microscopy Research and Technique 21: pp. 188-204. 1992) "The mammalian pineal gland is innervated by pheripheral sympathetic and parasympathetic nerve fibers as well as by nerve fibers originating in the central nervous system. The perikaya of the sympathetic fibers are located in the superior cervical ganglia. ..Both noradrenaline and neuropeptide Y are contained in these neurons. The parasympathetic fibers originate from perikara in the pterygopalatine ganglia. The neuropeptides. vasoactive intestinal peptide and peptide histidine isoleucine. at present in these fibers. The fibers of the central innervation originate predominantly from perikarya located in hypothalamic and limbic forebrain structures as well as from perikarya in the optic system." Sandyk, R., Relevance of the habenular complex to neuropsychiatry: a review and hypothesis, Intern. J. Neuroscience, 61: pp. 189-219, 1991) "the habenular complex provides and important (nerve fiber) link between the limbic forebrain (brain stem limbic system, dinosaur brain) and the midbrain (Androglynou.s pre-Adamic man. Adam Kadmon). ..there is growing evidence of the presence of anatomical and functional interactions between the habenular complex and the pineal gland."

These three nerve pathways were defined in the Kemetic literature as the paths of Osiris (Neophyte, male. right pathway, right branch of the tree of life, sympathetic, active), Isis (Intelligence, female, left pathway, left branch of the tree of life, parasympathetic passive), and Horus (Son of Light, child, middle pathway. central canal of spinal Cord, trunk of the tree of life, synthesis or union of the self affirmation (I am), Self reproduction, Facing God). Of Course this same theme is present upon viewing the Ankh the ancient African symbol for life, with a left arm (testicle), right arm (testicle) and middle spinal column with an oval on top (Black Dot, Womb (Uterus), skull-brain third ventricle, brain third ventricle being the location of the soul while in the physical body, third ventricle being the vault of initiation, the third ventricle being a C.S.F. fluid filled chamber with the pineal gland attached to the floor at the back end and the pituitary attached to the floor at the front end), the Holy chamber where the new child (fetus) is formed by self-affirmation (1 am), self-reproduction, the third ventricle being the tomb within the tomb into which has passed the Holy spirit., soul,. mind through Jet Black Melanin to become Holy Body, Facing God).

According to Murphy (Murphy, D. L., et. al., Effects of anti-depressant and other psychotropic drugs on melatonin release and pineal gland function, J. Neutal Transm. (Suppl.) 21: pp 291-309 1986) the sympathetic nerve pathway to the pineal is 1. light. 2. eye, 3. retinohypothalamic tract, 4. suprachiastmatic nuclei of hypothalmus, 5. medial forebrain bundle, 6. brain stem reticular formation 7. spinal Cord, 8. superior cervical ganglion, 9. pineal gland. and 10. melatonin/serotonin.

MELANIN AND THE PINEAL GLAND, SELECT REFERENCES FOR THE PINEAL GLAND/EYE OF HERO FROM THE KEMETIC COFFIN TEXTS

A STUDY OF ANCIENT AFRICAN HISTORY REVEALS THAT THE HUMAN MELANIN SYSTEM FUNCTIONS AS A HOLY BLACK BODY (HBB) AS THE EYE OF THE SOUL TO PRODUCE INNER VISION, TRUE SPIRITUAL CONSCIOUS-NESS, CREATIVE GENIUS, BEATIFIC VISION, TO BECOME GODLIKE, AND TO HAVE CONVERSATION WITH THE IMMORTALS (ANCESTORS). THE EYE OF INNER VISION FOR ALL HUMANS IS THE EYE OF HERU (HORUS, HERMES, MERCURY, SERAPIS, JESUS). THIS EYE IS THE "MESSENGER OF LIGHT" OF INNER VISION THAT IS A DOORWAY TO THE LIGHT OF THE ONE ETERNAL INTERNAL SUN (RA) THAT SHINES THROUGH ALL LIFE. The physicians of ancient Kemit wrote extensively about the Eye of Hem in their Great Books, The Old Kingdom Pyramid Texts (3,200?-2,100 B.C.E.), Middle Kingdom Coffin Texts (2,100- 1,675 B.C.E.), New Kingdom version of the Ptolemic Edfu Texts 332-30 B.C.E. (R. *King. African Origin of Biological Psychiatry,* 3rd Printing, 1994; U. B. & U. S. Communications Systems; 912 W. Pembroke Ave., Hampton, Va. 23669.) These African female and male professors were of the order Pastophori in the Per Ankh (House of Life) section of the Kemetic University System (Mystery System), which had existed as an intact Educational Academy for over 4,000 years before the founding of the Greek Library and Museum of Alexandria in Alexandria, Egypt in the Third century B. C. (George James, *Stolen Legacy,* 2nd Printing by U. B. & U. S. Communications Systems, 912 W. Pembroke Ave., Hampton, Va., 23669).

Perhaps we students may study and reflect upon the writings of our ancestors as offered in the Kemetic Great Books. For example, please consider these brief quotations from the Kemetic Foffin Texts. (Faulkner, R. 0., *The Ancient Egyptian Coffen Texts, V.* 1-111, Aris & Phillips, Ltd., Warminister, Wilts, England, 1978) "Send out your soul, that it may see with its eyes; such is Hem when he has reappeared in glory and has fashioned his bodily Eye. ..Is the soul Eye stronger than the gods? So say I to my father Atum. Strength has gone forth to me from your mouth, and it means that I have become Hem who is strongest among the gods, and Seth has fallen because of me, I have made his confederacy slip because of that account on which he wandered. ..I am Horus who lifted up his Eye. which appeared besouled, high and mighty; it consumes the river." (Faulkner, V.1, Section 316, pp 238-240.

"Take the Eye of Heru and be pleased with it, put the Eye of Hem on your brow. O Hem who is N, take the Eye of Hem, for it belongs to you, it belongs to your body, put it on yourself, provide yourself with it, for it will provide you as a god; lift up what is on you, which is on the brow of Heru." (Faulkner, V.3, section 845, pp. 30d).

"ON, Hem has attached his Eye to your forehead for you in its name of 'Great of Magic."

ON, take that of which the gods are afraid just as they are afraid of Heru.

ON, take the Eye of Hem, against which Seth acted.

ON, take the Eye of Heru, the half of which he saw the hand of Seth when he snached it.

ON, take the white Eye of Hem which he rescued from Seth when he snatched it.

ON, take the Eye of Hem, some of which he stole. ON, let him be far from you.

ON, take the Eye of Hem which hung from the hands of his children.

ON, take the water which is in the Eye of Hem, do not let go of it." (Faulkner, V.111, section 846, pp. 31)

"I am the Bull of Offerings, possessor of five loaves in the temple; three loaves are in the sky and two loaves are on earth. I bathe in the pools of the Netherwold. I ascend to the place of Shu belonging to the sky. What Seth detests is the Eye of Hem, and I will not eat faeces; what I detest is urine, and I will never drink it, just as Seth detested the Eye of Heru after the judgement in the great Prince-mansion which is in On. If one gives him to you, fighting will not be stopped, uproar will not be suppressed, the mottled cattle will not move about for themselves, Seth will swallow the Eye of Hem for himself after the judgement in the great Prince-mansion which is in On, and if you give this to me, there will be no coming into being or existing." (Faulkner, V.11, section 587, pp. 190).

"Heru has put gold on his Eye. O Hem who is N, take the Eye of Heru on which he has put gold, it is yours forever .

ON Heru who is N, I cause the two Eyes of Heru to go up for you to your face. I place for their (. ..) on you in their name of the Two Great of Magic.

ON Hero who is N, Heru gives his Eye, and it will guide you on the path, your throat will be opened by means of it, and the water in it is yours forever." (Faulkner, V.111, section 861, pp. 39)

ON, I give you the Eye of Hem, because of which the gods were merciful.

ON, I give you the Eye of Hem; betake yourself to it. ON, I give you the Eye of Hem which they guarded.

ON, I give you the lesser Eye of Heru, of which Seth ate.

ON, I give you the Eye of Hem, with which your mouth is opened. The pupil which is in the Eye of Hem, eat it.

ON, I give you the Eye of Hem, and you will not be ill. (Faulkner, section 157, V.1, pp. 135-136)

MELANIN AND THE PINEAL GLAND, SELECT REFERENCES FOR THE PINEAL GLAND IN THE CHRISTIAN BIBLE, GEN. 32:22-31

A STUDY OF ANCIENT AFRICAN HISTORY REVEALS HOW THE HUMAN MEI.ANIN SYSTEM FUNCTIONS AS A WHOLE BUCK MELANIN SYSTEM TO BE THE EYE OF THE SOUL TO PRODUCE INNER VISION, TRUE SPIRITUAL CON-SCIOUSNESS, CREATIVE GENRJS, BEATIFIC VISION, TO BECOME GODLIKE, AND TO HA VE CONVERSATION WITH THE IMMORTALS (ANCESTORS). THE EYE OF INNER VISION FOR ALL HUMANS IS THE EYE OF HERU (HORUS, HERMES, MERCURY, SERAPIS, JESUS) WHICH WAS GIVEN TO HORUS BY TEHUTI (THOTH) THE GOD OF MAGIC, SCI-ENCE AND WRITING, UNDER THE DIRECTION OF HIS FEMALE COMPANION, GODDESS SEFKET -AABUT, PRESI-DENT OF THE LIBRARY, SHE WHO IS PROVIDED WITH SEVEN HORNS." (Budge, Wallace, *The Gods of the Egyptians, Dover Publications,* N. Y. V. 1 pp. 426-4271969).

THIS LIGHT IS THE "MESSENGER OF LIGHT" OF THE ONE ETERNAL INTERNAL SUN THAT SHINES THROUGH ALL LIFE. FROM THE GREAT BOOKS OF ANCIENT KEMIT (PYRAMID TEXTS, COFFIN TEXTS. BOOK OF THE COMING FORTH BY DAY (BOOK OF THE DEAD), PTOLEMIC EDFU TEXTS. 42 BOOKS OF TEHUTI) ARE THE CORE TEXTS FROM WHICH WERE CONSTRUCTED THE OTHER GREAT BOOKS OF RELIGION SUCH AS THE CHRISTIAN BIBLE. "That which is known as the Christian religion existed among the ancients, and never did not exist; from the beginning of the human race until the time when Christ came in the flesh, at which time the true religion, which already existed began to be called Christianity." (St. Augustine, Retractt. I, xiii, cited by Dr. Alvin Boyd Kuhn, Shadow of the Third Century, Elizabeth, N. J., Academy Press, pp. 3, 1949, John G. Jackson, Christianity Before Christ, American Atheist Press, Austin Texas, pp. 1, 1985).

Major sections of the Great Books of Ancient Kemet were the product of the discoveries and revelations of African female and male physician professors of The Order Pastophori, Per Ankh (House of Life) Section of the Kemetic University System (Mystery System). This University system, was the "BACKBONE" OF KEMETIC (EGYPTIAN) CULTURE," existing as an intal.1 Educational Academy before the Hebrews and over 4,000 years before the Greek Library and Museum of Alexandria in Alexandria, Egypt in the third century B.C., (Ben-Jochanna, Yosef, *African Origins of the Major Western Religions,* Black Classic Press, Baltimore, Md.)

Thus, there are references to the EYE OF HERU in the Kemetic Great Books to history, anatomy, chemistry, and biological psychiatry and there are similar "CLINICAL MEDICINE QUATI-TATIVE" references for the EYE OF THE SOUL, EYE OF HERU, PINEAL GLAND, in the Christian Bible. Perhaps we students may study and reflect upon the fragments of the writings of our ancestors as they appear in the HOLY BOOK, THE BIBLE OF CHIRSTIAN-ITY IN Genesis 32, 22-31.

"And he rose up that night, and took his two wives, and his two women-servants, and his eleven sons, and passed over the ford Jabbok.

"And he took them, and sent them over the brook, and sent over that he had.

"And Jacob was left alone; and there wrestled a man with him until the breaking of day.

"And when he saw that he prevailed not against him, he touched the hollow of his thigh; and the hollow of Jacob's thigh was out of joint, as he wrestled with him.

"And he said. Let me go, for the day breaketh. And he said, I will not let thee go, except thou bless me.

"And he said unto him, What is thy name? And he said, Jacob.

"And he said, Thy name shall be called no more Jacob, but Israel: for as a prince has thou power with god and with men, and has prevailed.

"And Jacob asked him, and said, Tell me, I pray they, thy name? And he blessed him there.

" And Jacob called the name of the place Peniel: for I have seen God face to face, and my life is preserved-

"And as he passed over Peniel the sun rose upon him, and he halted upon his thigh."

In this biblical quotation are references to the NAME, PINEAL GRAND (PENIEL, PENUEL), describing an EVENT, (NAME CHANGE), in an ANATOMICAL SITE, (HOLLOW OF THIGH), by TWO FORMS OF ENVIRONMENTAL LIGHT , (NIGHT, SUNLIGHT), that control the pineal gland release of the hormone MELATONIN during MOON LIGHT NIGHT and SERO-TONIN during SUNLIGHT, DA YTIME.

Perhaps one may consider the symbolic interpretation of key words found in this quotation. (Metaphysical Bible Dictionary, Unity School of Christianity, Unity Village, Missouri-l. Peniel-turned toward God; face of God; within the presence of God; Contenance of god; vision of God: recognition of Glld; beholden of God; under-standing of God. Metaphysical - The inner realization of the divine presence, of having succeeded through prayer in attaining the divine favor and blessing that have been sought. (turned toward God); 2. Israel-contending for God, striving for God; who prevails with God; a prince with God; dominion with God; rulership with God. (ISRAEL, ISRAEL (THE GOD), THE ETERNAL INTERNAL SUN) Metaphysical -The Mind controls the body through the nerves, and a great nerve, the sciatic, runs down the leg through the hollow of the thigh. The will acts directly through this nerve an when the individual, through his mentality or understanding (Jacob), exercises his I AM (SOUL, HIGHER MIND) power upon the natural man in an attempt to make unity between Spirit and the divine -natural, there is a letting go of human will (Jacob's thigh out of joint). A great light of understanding breaks in the struggling soul when it discovers that there is a divine-natural body, and it clings to that inner life and strength in perpetual vigor. Strength in both spiritual and material. KM-WR (Perfect Black).

MELANIN, INNER VISION, BLACK SYMBOLISM, ISLAM AND THE EI'KAABA IN MECCA

A STUDY OF ANCIENT AFRICAN HISTORY REVEALS AN FARL Y AFRICAN DEFINITION OF THE HUMAN MELANIN SYSTEM AS A (WHOLE) HOLY BLACK BODY (HBB) THAT SERVES AS THE EYE OF THE SOUL TO PRODUCE INNER VISION, TRUE SPIRITUAL CONSCIOUSNESS, CREATIVE GENIUS, BEATIFIC VISION, TO BECOME GODLIKE, AND TO HAVE CONVERSATION WITH THE IMMORTALS (ANCESTORS). THE PURPOSE OF ANCIENT AFRICAN EDUCATION WAS TO PROVIDE KNOWLEDGE AND DEVELOPMENT OF THE WILL OF THE STUDENT THAT ALLOWED SALVATION (FREEDOM) OF THE SOUL FROM THE FETTERS (CHAINS) OF THE PHYSICAL BODY. (George James, *Stolen Legacy, Chapter3,* U. B. & U. S. Communications Systems, Inc.).

THIS EYE IS THE "MESSENGER OF LIGHT" OF THE ONE ETERNAL SUN THAT SHINES THROUGH ALL LIFE. FROM THE GREAT BOOKS OF ANCIENT KEMIT (PYRAMID TEXTS, COFFIN TEXTS, BOOK OF THE COMING FORTH BY DA Y (Book of the Dead), PTOLEMIC EDFU TEXTS, 42 BOOKS OF TEHUTI) ARE THE CORE TEXTS FROM WHICH WERE CONSTRUCTED THE OTHER GREAT BOOKS OF REUGION SUCH AS THE HOL Y BOOK, THE QUR'AN OF ISLAM.

"629 c. e., A. H. 7, was the year (PROPHET) Muhammad returned to Mecca from Medina, where he was forced to run and hide. It marked the date when the treaty agreement between (PROPHET) Muhammad's government he had formed with Bilal in their six years of exile at the Oasis of Yathrib, in Medina, and the government he had fled in Mecca. Between these two dates (622-629 C. E. or A. H. 1- 7, however, the government in Mecca witnessed a mass conversion of its citizens from the worship of the goddess AI'lat and El Ka'aba (the black sone meteorite from Ethiopia, East Africa). These established religions for centuries' duration had represented the moral and religious fabrics of the government in Mecca. ..(PHOPHET) Muhammad triumphantly returned to Mecca. He and his faith followers in Islam (the "new religion") adopted Mecca as their "HOL Y CITY ." They also adopted El Ka'aba (the Black Stone Metorite from Ethiopia). But they completely rejected paying any further tribute to the Goddess Al'lat, who was replaced by the God AI'lah. ..The following are the Goddesses of Islam who became the. .."DAUGHTERS OF AL'LAH:" Al-lat, the Sun Goddess. AI-Manat, the Goddess of Venus. *Al-Uzzah*, the Fortune Goddess." *(*Ben-Jochannan, *African Origins of the Major Western Religions,* Black *Classic* Press: *Baltimore,* Maryland, pp. 214-215).

Concerning the actual viewing (external and internal vision) of the El Ka'aba in Mecca, a follower of islam observed, "He means that the least of the sciences of nearness (proximity to God) is that when you look (consciousness, attention, meditation) at anything, sensibly or intellectually or otherwise, you I should be conscious of beholding God with a vision clearer than your vision I of that thing. There are diverse degrees in this matter. Some mystics say that t they never see anything without seeing God before it, or 'with it'; or they say that they see nothing but God. A certain Sufi said, I made pilgrimage and saw the Ka'ba.' This is the perception of one who is veiled. Then he said, 'I made , the pilgrimage again, and I saw both the Ka 'ba and the Lord of the Ka'ba. This is contemplation of the Self-subsistence through which everything subsists, he saw the Ka'ba. Then he said, I made the pilgrimage a third time, and I saw the Lord of the Ka'ba, but not the Ka'ba. This the station of waqfat (passing-away in essence). In the present case the author is referring to contemplation of the Self-subsistence." (Nicholson, Reynold *A.,* The Mystics of Islam, Schocken Book, New York, pp. 57-58,1975) .

Thus, for many followers of Islam the experience of viewing the Black Stone Meteorite El Ka'aba in Mecca evokes the inner vision image and experience of God. This inner vision event was likely to have been experienced by the same Africans who brought the Black Stone from Ethoipia to Arabia long before the birth of the PROPHET MOHAMET. It is equally important to note that in Kemet, the genetic child of Ethiopia, Black Stones were given Divine Value. Black stones were often placed as the all Black pyramiadon cap stones upon the top of pyramids, an all black stone room (rose granite being a black granite with flecks of red as the King's chamber is the highest room in the interior of the Great Pyramid of Giza, and a special system of linear measurement being used by Kamites when working in Black Stone, the Black Cubit or nilometic cubit. (King, Richard, African Origin of Biological Psychiatry, pp. 22) The ancient African professors of the ancient Kemetic University, The Mystery System of Kemet, built pyramids as temple symbolic replicas of the human temple, the human body, which contained the human soul, the top of the human body containing a veiled, BLACK EYE OF INNER VISION, THE EYE OF HERU, THE PINEAL GLAND WHICH WAS PART OF THE HOLY BLACK BODY (HBB) AND SERVED TO MEDIATE THE HUMAN RELATION-SHIP TO SUNLIGHT AND MOONLIGHT.

"Osiris as light giver in the moon was tom into fourteen pieces during the latter half of the lunation by the evil Sut, the opposing power of darkness. He was put together again and reconstituted by his son, beloved Horns, the young solar god. This representation could not have been made until it was known that lunar light was replenished monthly from the solar source. Then Horns as the sungod and the vanquisher of Sut, the power of darkness, could be called the reconsitutor of Osiris in the Moon. (Gerald Massey, Ancient Egypt, V. 1, pp. 187)

"On the monuments Osiris is sometimes seen as a human-headed mummy, holding the emblems of power, and wearing on his head the image of a full moon within a CRESCENT ...There were two sets of Mysteries. Osiris (male, Sun) was god of the Greater Mysteries, and Isis (Female, Moon) was worshipped in the Lesser Mysteries." (Jackson, John, Christianity Before Christ, p. 137)

MELANIN, NAME DERIVATION FROM THE GREEK WORD MELANOS. KEMETIC NAME FOR BLACK BEING KM

A STUDY OF ANCIENT AFRICAN HISTORY REVEALS AN EARLY AFRICAN DEFINITION OF THE HUMAN MELANIN SYSTEM AS A (WHOLE) HOLY BLACK BODY (HBB) THAT SERVES AS THE EYE OF THE SOUL TO PRODUCE INNER VISION, TRUE SPIRITUAL CONSCIOUSNESS, CREATIVE GENIUS, BEATIFIC VISION, TO BECOME GODLIKE, AND TO HAVE CONVERSATION WITH THE IMMORT *ALS* (ANCESTORS). THE PURPOSE OF ANCIENT AFRICAN EDUCATION WAS TO PROVIDE KNOWLEDGE AND DEVELOPMENT OF THE WILL OF THE STUDENT THAT ALLOWED SALVATION (FREEDOM) OF THE SOUL FROM THE FETTERS (CHAINS) OF THE PHYSICAL BODY. (George James, *Stolen Legacy, Chapter* 3, U. B. & U. S. Communications Systems, Inc.). MELANIN IS THE CHEMICAL OF LIFE. THE CHEMICAL OF THE SOUL, A TRANSPHYSICAL DOORWAY THROUGH WHICH THE ENERGY WA YES OF THE HOLY SOUL, SPIRIT, AND MIND PASS TO TAKE FORM AS THE HOLY BLACK BODY. ANCIENT AFRICANS IN KEMIT (EGYPT) VIEWED ALL THE CONTENTS OF AMENT A (THE UNDERWORLD=PERSONAL SUBCONSCIOUS [MIND], SUPER-CONSCIOUS [SOUL], COLLECTIVE UNCONSCIUOS [SPIRIT] AS JET BLACK IN COLOR.

Melanin is a Greek name for the color black which was taken form the Greek word Melanos which means Black. The ancient Kemetic (Egyptian) name for black was KM (pronounced in English as keme). Budge has written, (Budge, Wallis, Egyptian magic, Dover Publications, Inc., New York, 1971, "One of the oldest names of Egypt is "Kamt", "Qemt," a word which means "black" or "dusky," ...the Christian Egyptian or Copts transmitted the word under the form Kheme to the Greeks, Romans, Syrians and Arabs. At a very early period the Egyptians were famous for their skill in the working of metals and in their attempts to transmute them, and, according to

Greek writers, they employed quicksilver (mercury) in the processes whereby they separated the metals gold and silver from the native ore. From these processes there resulted a (jet) "black" powder or substance which was supposed to possess the most marvelous powers, and to contain in it the individualities of the various metals; and in it their actual substances were incorporated. In a msytical manner this "black" powder was identified with the body which the god Osiris was known to possess it in the underworld, and to both were attributed magical qualities, and both were thought to be sources of life and power. ..the belief that magical powers existed in fluxes and alloys; and the art of manipulating the metals, were described by the name "Khemeia," that is to say, "the preparation of the black ore" (or "powder") which was regarded as the active principle in the transmutation of metals. To this name the Arabs affixed the article al, and thus the word Al-Khemeia, or Alchemy." Please consider the literal meaning of the word Al-Kemiea or Alchemy which is AL (THE GOD)- Khemeia (BLACK) or THE BLACK GOD (ALCHEMY).

Please Consider, the words of Marimba Ani (Ani, Marimba, Yurugu, An African-Centered Critiqe of European Cultural Thought and Behavior , African World Press, Inc., Trenton, New Jersey, pp. 469-471, 1994)," with less melanin (Europeans) we could expect an over-all lower level of nervous system integration, less activity of the pineal gland, and greater instance of pineal calcification. This in turn, might limit access to right-brain function associated with the pineal gland; e.g., the development of intuitiveness, holistic, "global" thinking, the ability to comprehend spiritual truths. .. melanin and the pineal gland are the keys to a deeper spiritual consciousness on which level human beings can integrate their understanding/knowledge to reach metaphysical truths that unlock the doors of the dark unconscious, bringing with it an emotional, and psychological sense of security: a oneness with self, an inner peace ...the (European) fear of their unconscious, ancestral selves manifested as a fear of others. ..Africans-their "mothers," "parents," their source-becomes the most feared "other." They feared that which they were incapable of knowing, which came to represent to them the sensation of a loss of control, of chaos, and disorder. For spiritual reality becomes overwhelming if one loses one's connection. ..blackness came to represent evil (for Europeans and mental Slave Africans) and why the 'dark side" became threatening. blackness indeed was the spiritual, metaphysical realm to which European had little if any access. The "dark side" of this was the inner vision of the unconscious that opened the door to communication with the ancestral symbols and wisdom."

Please Consider the writings of our Kemitic Ancestors, Coffin Texts, of over 4,000 years ago (Faulkner, R. 0., The Ancient Egyptian Coffin Texts, V. 1-111, Airs & Phillips, Ltd., Warminister, Wilts, England, V.1, pp. 135- 136,1978)." It so happened that Re' (Sun God Ra) said to Heru: 'Let me see your Eye since this happened to it.' He looked at it and said, 'Look at the (black) stroke with your hand covering up the sound Eye which is there.' Heru looked at that stroke and said: 'Behold, I am seeing it as altogether white.' and that is how the oryx came into being. And Re' said, 'Look again at yonder black pig.' And Heru looked at this black pig, and Horns cried out because of the condition of his injured Eye, saying, 'Behold, my Eye is like that first wound which Seth Inflicted on my Eye,' and Horns became unconscious in his presence. And Re' said: 'Put him on his bed until he is well.' It so happened that Seth had transformed himself into a pig and had projected a wound into his Eye. The pig is detestable to Horns."

Jung (Jung, C. G., Psychology and Alchemy, V. 12, The Collected i Works of c. G. Jung, Bollingen Series XX, Princeton University Press, pp. 389 1974), has written, "The real nature of matter was unknown to the alchemist: ...In seeking to explore it he projected the unconscious (Amenta) into the darkness of matter in order to illuminate it. ..Strictly speaking, projection is never made; it happens. ..it was an involuntary occurance."

Please consider an African vision of the Soul (angel) in Black Amenta, in the tomb of the Body, awaiting salvation to guide one up the path of life.(Front Book Cover picture of the 2 human forms, the large angel soul of higher personality, and the small ego [lower personality, from the Black cube] Holy Black Body, physical body self reproduced through the melanin door, melanin the chemical life whose central atom is carbon which exists in nature in the shape of a cube.)

MELANIN MOLECULE AND STRUCTURAL PROPERTIES FOR THE RECEPTION OF VISIBLE LIGHT AND U. V. LIGHT

A STUDY OF ANCIENT AFRICAN HISTORY REVEALS AN EARLY AFRICAN DEFINITION OF THE HUMAN MELANIN SYSTEM AS A WHOLE BODY BLACK MELANIN SYSTEM THAT SERVES AS THE EYE OF THE SOUL TO PRODUCE INNER VISION, TRUE SPIRITUALCONSCIOUSNESS, CREATIVE GENIUS, BEATIFIC VISION, TO BECOME GODLIKE, AND TO HAVE CONVERSATION WITH THE IMMORTALS (ANCESTORS). THE PURPOSE OF ANCIENT AFRICAN EDUCATION WAS TO PROVIDE KNOWLEDGE AND DEVELOPMENT OF THE WILL OF THE STUDENT THAT ALLOWED SALVATION (FREEDOM) OF THE SOUL FROM THE FETTERS (CHAINS) OF THE PHYSICAL BODY. (George James, *Stolen Legacy, Chapter* 3, U. B. & U. S. Communications Systems, Inc.). MELANIN IS THE CHEMICAL OF LIFE, THE CHEMICAL OF THE SOUL, A TRANSFORMATION DOORWAY THROUGH WHICH THE ENERGY WAVES OF THE HOLY SOUL, SPIRIT, AND MIND PASS TO TAKE FORM AS THE HOLY BODY. ANCIENT AFRICANS IN KEMIT (EGYPT) VIEWED ALL THE CONTENTS OF AMENTA (THE UNDERWORLD=PERSONAL SUBCONSCIOUS [MIND], SUPER-CONSCIOUS [SOUL], COLLECTIVE UNCONSCIUOS [SPIRIT] AS JET BLACK IN COLOR.

MELANIN IS THE CHEMICAL OF LIFE, THE CHEMICAL OF THE SOUL, A TRANSFORMATIONAL DOORWAY THROUGH WHICH THE ENERGY WAVES OF THE HOLY SOUL, SPIRIT, AND MIND PASS TO TAKE FORM AS THE HOLY BODY. ANCIENT AFRICANS IN KEMIT EGYPT) VIEWED ALL THE CONTENTS OF AMENTA (THE UNDERWORLD, PERSONAL SUBCONSCIOUS [MIND], SUPER-CONSCIOUS [SOUL], COLLECTIVE UNCONSCIOUS [SPIRIT] AS JET BALCK IN COLOR. (Pinakoff, Alexandre, The Shrines of Tutankhamun) Perhaps we may STUDY, APPRECIATE, and REFLECT upon the writings of our ANCESTORS as they appear in the GREAT BOOKS of ancient Kemet (PYRAMID TEXTS, COF-FIN TEXTS. BOOK OF THE COMING FORTH BY DAY [BOOK OF THE DEAD]). These ancient African Texts Contain actual MIND MAPS for Guiding the movement of LIFE (LIGHT) through the transformational "FINE STUFF (MELANIN) DOOR between the different realms of LIFE (LIGHT).

THERE ARE MANY FORMS OF LIGHT THAT REACH THE SURFACE OF OUR PLANET SUCH AS MOONLIGHT, AND MANY DIFFERENT FORMS OF STAR LIGHT GALACTIC CENTER BLACK HOLES, NEUTRON STARS, RED GIANTS, PULSARS, QUASARS), RADIATION FROM THE ORIGINAL BIRTH OF THIS DIMENSION OF THE PHYSICAL UNIVERSE [THE BIG BANG] AND THE LIGHT (LIFE) FROM OUR SUN. THERE IS ALSO AN ETERNAL INTERNAL SUN THAT SUP-PORTS ALL DEMENSIONS OF ALL UNIVERSES.

Concerning the light of the sun of our solar system Ceserini has written, (Cesarini, J., Photo,-induced events in the human Melanocytic system: photoaggression and photoprotection, Pigment cell Research, l: pp. 223-233, 1988) "The spectral power distribution of the sunlight is continuous, extending from X-Rays to radio-waves. It has been divided into wavelength regions, based on well recognized biological effects, corresponding to the absorptions by chromophores in specific wavebands.

After absorption through the terrestrial upper and lower atmosphere, the solar spectrum reaching the earth surface is composed of UVB, UV A, visible and infrared radiations. Ozone is responsible in the upper atmosphere for a complete absorption of UVC, while the lower atmosphere absorbs most of the UVB. In the Dead Sea (400 meters below sea level), only traces of UV below 320 nm are detected.

Among the chromophores, melanins, present in the stratum corneum and stratum Malpighi, act as a filter, shielding other chormophores, like DNA, from incident UVR."

In humans there are two different types of melanin, eumelanin, black or brown in color, and pheomelanin, red to yellow in color. ito (Ito, Shosuke, High-performance, liquid chromatography (HPLC) anaylsis of eu-and pheomelanin in melanogenesis, J. Invest. Dermatol. 110: 166S-171S, 1993, has reported that it is difficult to distinguish between dark brown eumelanin and reddish brown pheomelanin by visual inspection. The differences between the two types of melanin is determined best by differences in elemental content. Eumelanin has a sulfur element content of 0-1% while pheomelanin has a sulfur content of 9-12%. The presence of large amounts of sulfur in pheomelanin produces important structural changes by promoting short chains of monomer units as compared to the long chains monomer units found in eumelanin (Barnes, Carol, 1993). Ito (1993) reported, "ellipsoidal-lamellar melanosomes are found associated with eumelanogenesis." Ito also noted that although eumelanin and pheomelanin are both produced from the amino acid tyrosine the high sulfur content of phoemelanin leads to the production of intermediate forms of 2-S-Cysteinyldopa and 5-S-Cysteinyldopa which then yield a benothiazine derivative and finally pheomelanin. These three inter- mediate forms of pheomelanin are known to induce cancer by binding to DNA upon exposure to UV light. They do not exist in eumelanin formation. (Koch, w. H. and Chedekel, M. R., Photoinitiated DNA damage by melanogenic intermediates invivo, Photochem. Phototbio. 44: pp. 703-710,1986) Humans with high skin phoemelanin have a high frequency of squamous cell carcinoma of the skin, basal cell carcinoma of the skin, and in all western countries skin melanomas are doubling every ten years. (Cesarini, 1988)

In 1977 the human population was divided into six types by skin sensitivity to phototoxic reaction (sunburn) of psoralen-UV A psoriatic patients on day 7 following irradiation of 1 hour of midday sun in June under 40 degree latitude- Type I, Caucasian, always burns without tan, Type ll, caucasian, always burns and light tan, Type II, Caucasian, slight burn and good tan, Type IV, Caucasian, no burn and dark tan, Type V, Monogoloids, Middle Eastern population and metiss (mixed human racial type), and type VI, African and American Blacks. (Meleski, J. W., Tenbaum, L., Parrish, J. A. , Fitzpatirck, T. *B.,* Bleich, H. L., and 28 participating investigators. Oral methoxypsoralen photochemotherapy for the treatment of psoriasis, J. Invest. Dermato. 68: pp. 328-335, 1977) This is critical data for Type I and Type II caucasians are at high risk for the development of various forms of skin cancer during the course of their adult life because of a lack of skin eumelanin, and the presence of toxic products from their skin pheomelanin upon exposure to uv light.

Furthermore there are differences in the number and shape of melannosomes, the vesicle for melanin storage within the skin melanocyte. This vesicle is transferred into skin cells to organize into a layer over the skin cell nucleus for protection of skin cell DNA. Cesarini 1988) using the definition of six phototypes for melanosomes found that for Types I and II the melanosome." are round and fewer in number, Type III a mixture of round and oval shape, and Type VI with numerous ovoid melanosomes- Types I and II have a less effective (melasome dense) shield over skin DNA.

MELANIN AND NEUROMELANIN

A STUDY OF ANCIENT AFRICAN HISTORY REVEALS AN EARLY AFRICAN DEFINITION OF 'THE HUMAN MELANIN SYSTEM AS A (WHOLE) HOLY BLACK BODY (HBB) THAT SERVES AS THE EYE OF THE SOUL TO PRODUCE INNER VISION, TRUE SPIRITUAL CONSCIOUSNESS, CREATIVE GENIUS, BEATIFIC VISION, TO BECOME GOD-LIKE, AND TO HAVE CONVERSATION WITH THE IMMORTALS (ANCESTORS). THE PURPOSE OF ANCIENT AFRICAN EDUCATION WAS TO PROVIDE KNOWLEDGE AND DEVELOPMENT OF THE WILL OF THE STUDENT THAT ALLOWED SALVATION (FREEDOM) OF THE SOUL FROM THE FETTERS (CHAINS) OF THE PHYSICAL BODY. (George *James, "Stolen Legacy,* Chapter 3; U. B. & U. S. Communications Systems, Inc. 912 W. Pembroke Ave., Hampton, Va. 23669.

MELANIN IS THE CHEMICAL OF LIFE, THE CHEMICAL OF THE SOUL, A TRANSFORMATION DOORWAY THROUGH WHICH THE ENERGY W A YES OF THE HOL Y SOUL, SPIRIT , AND MIND PASS TO TAKE FORM AS THE HOLY BODY. ANCIENT AFRICANS IN KEMIT (EGYPT) VIEWED ALL THE CONTENTS OF AMENTA (THE UNDERWORLD, PERSONAL SUBCONSCIOUS [MIND] SUPER- CONSCIOUS [SOUL], COLLECTIVE UNCONSCIOUS [SPIRIT] AS JET BLACK IN COLOR. (Pinakoff, Alexandre, *The Shrines of Tutankhamun)* Perhaps we may STUDY, APPRECIATE, and Reflect upon the writings of our ancestors, as they appear in THE GREAT BOOKS of ancient Kemet (PYRAMID TEXTS, COFFIN TEXTS, BOOK OF THE COMING FORTH BY DA Y [BOOK OF THE DEAD]). These ancient AFRICAN TEXTS contain actual MIND MAPS for GUIDING the movement of LIFE (LIGH1) through the transphysical "FINE STUFF" (MELANIN) DOOR between the different realms of LIFE (LIGHT).

Strzelecka (Strzelecka, T., A hypothetical structure of melanin and it's relation to biology, Physiol. Chem. Phys. 14: pp. 233-237, 1982) has presented insights into the role of the structure of melanin in absorbing LIGHT (LIFE), "one of the most interesting features of the melanin is its optical absorption spectrum; the absorption coefficient is nearly constant between 400 and 700 nm yet rises rapidly toward the shorter wavelength." (Crippa, P. R., Cristoletti, V., Romeo, N., A. band model for the melanin deduced from optical absorption and photoconductivity experiments. Biochem. Biophys. Acta. 538: pp. 164, 1978) Melanin was shown by McGinness that when absorbing ultrasound in the 1 MHz region converted into a form that killed cancer cells. (McGinness, *I.* E., Corry, P. M., Amour, E., Melanin-binding drugs and ultrasound induced-cytotoxicity, Pigment Cell, 2: pp. 316, 1976) Strzelecka observed that synthetic melanin and natural melanin, hair melanin, have several similar but slightly different regions of optical absorption of light -synthetic melanin with three regions of absorption: 14:46-1.85 e V, 1.85 -3.5 eV, and ablJVe 3.5 eV which Correspond to LIGHT wavelength regions of 850- 670 nm, 670-355 nm, and below 355 nm. Hair melanin has two regions of absorption: 1:57-3.4 eV and above 3.4 eV which correspond to LIGHT wavelength regions of 790-365 nm and below 365 nm.

One part absorbed LIGHT in the visible range (1.57-3.4 eV). Whereas the second part of the melanin polymer absorbed LIGHT in the ultraviolet region (above 3.4 eV). Strzelecka accepted the theory of the melanin polymer being composed of two stacks of several planar groups parallel to each other. (Thatachari, Y., Structure of melanins, Ibid, l:pp. 158, 1973 and Kono, R., Yamaoka, T., Yoshizaki, H., McGinness, J. E., Anomalous absorption and dispersion of sound waves in diehtylamine melanin, J. Appl. Phys., 50: pp. 1236, 1980). The monomeric units in melanin have absorption in the visible UGHT region with the interaction between them resulting in stack shifts toward the longer visible LIGHT wavelengths. The melanin polymer was seen to have a "core" with monomer units bound to the "Core" that during degradation the stacks themselves can be destroyed but are still capable of absorbing LIGHT in the visible region. Strzelecka noted, "the core also becomes destroyed but still absorbs Uv (LIGHT) radiation. . .Probably that is the reason melanin was "chosen" in the evolution process as a substance that can best protect cells of the outer tissues against radiation damage, which explains why we find this polymer in so many species from plants to humans."

THIS APPLIES TO THE EUMELANIN FORM OF MELANIN, BLACK TO BROWN IN COLOR, BUT NOT PHAEOMELANIN, WHICH IS RED TO YELLOW IN COLOR. PHEOMELANIN BEHAVES DIFFERENTLY WHEN EXPOSED TO UV LIGHT. (Menon, I. A., Persad, *S.,* Habennan, H. F., Kurian, C. *I.,* A compartive study of the physical and chemical properties of melanins isolated from human black and red hair. *I.* Invest. Dennatol., 80: pp. 202-206, 1983).

Cesarini (Cesarini, J., Photo-induced events in the human melanocytic system: photoagression and photoprotection, Pigment Cell Research, 1: pp. 223-233,1988) reported, "pheomelanin became mutagenic (produced cancer) after exposure to long-wave length UV -light, finding consistent with the UV- induced somatic mutation hypothesis for the origin of freckles. ..and the high susceptibility of redheads and blondes to sunlight-induced skin changes. Koch (Koch, W. H., and Chedekel, M. R., Photoiniated DNA damage by melanogenic intermediates in vitro, Photochem. Photobiol., 44: pp. 703- 710, 1986) de.."l-Tibed photo-initiated DNA damages by melanogenic intermediates of 5-S-cysteinyl-dopa origin. The binding of this molecule to DNA is activated by the 300 nm UV -light together with the induction of single strand breaks in DNA. ..Menon (1983) found the red hair (pheomelanin) contained more S (sulfur) than black hair (eumelanin) melanins. ..It has been shown that the incidence of squamous cell carcinoma of the skin and basal cell carcinoma arise with high frequency in groups of people with blue-green eyes, clear Complexion, light and red hairs. ..in all western countries skin melanomas are doubling every ten years."

MELANIN AND THE ELECTROMAGNETIC THEORY OF LIFE

A STUDY OF ANCIENT AFRICAN HISTORY REVEALS THE AFRICAN DEFINITION OF THE HUMAN MELANIN SYS- TEM AS A (WHOLE) HOLY BLACK BOOK (HBB) THAT SERVES AS THE EYE OF THE SOUL TO PRODUCE INNER VISION, TRUE SPIRITUAL CONSCIOUSNESS, CREATIVE GENIUS, BEATIFIC VISION, TO BECOME GODLIKE, AND TO HAVE CONVERSATION WITH THE IMMORTALS (ANCES- TORS). THE PURPOSE OF ANCIENT AFRICAN EDUCATION WAS TO PROVIDE THE KNOWLEDGE AND DEVELOP- MENT OF THE WILL OF THE STUDENT THAT ALLOWED SAL- VATION(FREEDOM OF THE SOUL) FROM THE FETTERS (CHAINS) OF THE PHYSICAL BODY. (George James, Stolen Legacy, Chapter 3, U. B. & U. S. Communications Systems, Inc.) MELANIN IS THE CHEMICAL OF LIFE, THE CHEMICAL OF THE SOUL, A TRANSFORMA TIONAL *DOOR-WA YTHROUGH WHICH THE ENERGY WA VES OF THE HOLY* SOUL, SPIRIT, AND MIND PASS TO TAKE FORM AS THE HOLY BODY.

Melanin is present in brain cells, neurons, in many different sites throughout the brain. The Melanin found in such sites is known as neuromelanin. (Graham, D. G., On the Origin and Significance of Neuromelanin, Arch. Pathol Lab. Med. 103: pp. 359-362, 1979; Lindquist, N. G., Neuromelanin and its Possible Protective and Destructive Properties, Pigment Cell Research l: pp. 133-136, 1987; Bazelon, M., Studies on neuromelanin. 1. A melanin system in the human adult brainstem. Neurology, 17: pp. 512-519,1967; Fenichel, G. M., Studies on neuromelanin. II. Melanin in the brainstem of infants and children. Neurology, 18: pp. 817 -820, 1968; Lacy, M. Neuromelanin: A hypothetical component of bioelectronic mecha- nisms in brain function, Physiol. Chem. & Physics, 13: pp. 319-324, 1981; Lacy, M., Photon-electron coupling as a possible transducing mechanism in bioelectronic processes involving neuromelanin, J. theor. Bioi., 111:pp. 201-204,1984; ML-Ginness, J., A new view of pigmented neurons, J. theor. Bioi. 115: pp. 474-476, 1985; Marsden,

C. D., Brain melanin. In: Pigments in pathology. M. Wollman ed. Academic Press, New York, pp. 395- 420, 1969; Mann, D.M.A., The effect of aging on the pigmented nerve cell of the human locus coreuleus and substantial nigra, Acta Neuropathol. (Berl.) 47: pp. 93-97, 1979).

According to Lindquist (1987), "Many of the properties of neuromelanin are similar to those of other types of melanin, but neuromelanin differs from the melanin present melanocytes in some respects: it may be formed mainly by other enzymes than tyrosinase or, at least partly, autoxidatively ."

However, Lacy (1981) has reported, "Whereas tyrosinase, is involved in the formation of ocular-cutaneous (skin, eye) melanin, tyrosinase hydroxylase is probably involved in the formation of neuromelanin. Normal brain pigmentation is observed in abino rats and albino humans although they have a genetic deficiency of tyrosinase (critical enzyme required for melanin formation in skin). Tyrosinase has not been found in brain tissue, whereas tyrosinase hydroxylase not only is found, but occurs in the largest concentrations in those regions of the brain (substantia nigra and locus coeruleus) containing the greatest Concentrations of neuromelanin. (Neuromelanin in brain is formed by the enzyme thyrosine hydroxylase and in skin melanin is formed by the enzyme tyrosine.

It has been proposed that neuromelanill is actually an accumuating by- product of catecholamine metabolism. Studies by Kastin and co-workers (Kastin, 111. Melanin in the rat brain, Brain Res. Bull. 1: pp. 567, 1976), however, show that the concentration of neuromelanin in rat brain reaches adult levels sooner that the concentrations of catecholamines. The absence of Continuing Concomitant formation indicates that the two processes can be only indirectly related."

Lindquist (1987) noted, "Neuromelanin seems to be very stable and is not normally secreted from the cells where it is formed. Young individuals have small amounts of neuromelanin (Bazelon, 1967, Fenichel, 1968), but in man the pigment is accumulated in the neurons in substantia nigra and locus coeruleus up to 55-60 years of age, when the level of neuromelanin in these cells seems to slowly decrease (Marsden, 1969, Mann, 1979). The turnover of the neuromelanin seems to be extremely low; perhaps the only way of degradation is release of pigment granules from damaged neurons and phagocytosis by glia cells (Marsden, 1969)."

Lindquist cited two possible functional roles of neuromelanin the Conversion of harmful free radical chemicals into vibrational energy (phononelectron Coupling, Lacy, 1984) and the accumulation of chemical compounds such as amines and metals for long time periods with slow release of the agents in low, non-toxic concentrations.

Lindquist said, "It is possible that at least two compounds, MPTP and manganese, due to their direct or indirect neurotoxicity may cause lesions in pigment containing neurons secondary to their accumulation on the neuromelanin granules (Parkinson's disease, extra pyramidal disorders resembling Parkinson's disease). Many other compounds have melanin affinity. ..Among these agents one pesticide, paraquat, which is of interest because it is chemically related to a metabolite of MPTP. Paraquat has been found almost as toxic to the frog as this particular MPTP-metabolite (Barbeau, A., Compartive behavioral biochemical and pigmentary effects of MPTP , MPP +- and paraquat in Rana pipiens, Life Sci. 37: pp. 1529-1538, 1985). In recent epidemiological investigation, the highest prevalence rates of Parkinson's disease were found in rural agricultural areas of high pesticide use. (Barbeau, A., Environmental and genetic factors in the etiology of Parkinson's disease. Adv. Neurol., 45: pp. 299-306,1986)".

MELANIN AND THE TRANSFORMATION
OF THE FIVE SENSES

A STUDY OF ANCIENT AFRICAN HISTORY REVEALS THE AFRICAN DEFINITION OF THE HUMAN MELANIN SYSTEM AS A (WHOLE) HOLY BLACKBODY (HBB) THAT SERVES AS THE EYE OF THE SOUL TO PRODUCE INNER VISION, TRUE SPIRITUAL CONSCIOUSNESS, CREATIVE GENIUS, BEATIFIC VISION, TO BECOME GODLIKE, AND TO HAVE CONVERSATION WITH THE IMMORTALS (ANCESTORS). THE PURPOSE OF ANCIENT AFRICAN EDUCATION WAS TO PROVIDE THE KNOWLEDGE (ENERGY) AND DEVELOPMENT OF THE WILL (ENERGY) OF THE STUDENT THAT ALLOWED SALVATION (FREEDOM) OF THE SOUL (ENERGY) FROM THE FETTERS (CHAINS) OF THE PHYSICAL BODY. (George James, *Stolen Legacy, Chapter* 3, U. B. & U. S. C. S., Inc.). MELANIN IS THE CHEMICAL O F LIFE, THE CHEMICAL OF THE SOUL, A CONDUCTOR OF DYNAMIC TURNOVER AS A MUSICAL CHOIR, A TRANS- PHYSICAL DOORWAY THROUGH WHICH THE ENERGY WAVES OF THE HOLY SOUL, AND MIND PASS TO TAKE FORM AS THE HOLY BODY. ANCIENT AFRICANS IN KEMIT (EGYPT) VIEWED ALL CONTENTS OF AMENTA (THE UNDERWORLD=PERSONAL SUBCONSCIOUS [MIND], SUPERCONSCIOUS [SOUL], COLLECTIVE UNCONSCIOUS [SPIRIT] AS JET BLACK IN COLOR.

Pryse (Pryse, J. M., Apocalypse unsealed, [the drama of self conquest] Health Research, Mkelumne Hill, California, pp. 68,33-75,1965) in 1919 reported. "four planes of existence in the Apocalypse, as (1) the Sky (Spiritual World, Noetic Forces, (2) The Rivers and Springs, Psychic World (Earth, Physical World, Psychomental Forces, (3) The Sea (Phantasmal World, Animal-Psychic Forces), and (4) The Earth (Physical World, Vital Forces); while Compassing these four is the Air the Empyrean which is called the fifth world in the Ptolemaic system, although it really stands for the three formless planes (The Three Deific Hypostases (The Dragon of

61

Light)- The First Logos (God's Love), the Second Logos (Divine Ideation), and the Virgin (Primoridal Substance). Below the realm of the Dragon of Light and the realm of the Four Winds of Forn1 was composed of the The Beast (Phrenic Intellect), The Prostitute (The Gross Elements) and The Pseudo-Seer (Desire). Pryse said, "In literary (Rev. 1 :9) Construction of the Apocalypse follows to some extent the conventional Greek Drama. ..By sentimental literalists the Apocalypse is generally accepted as a record of visions actually seen by "the Seer of Patmos." This may also be a reference to Pythagoras, Yacub, or Jacob?

It is important to note that this model of the universe cites the fifth world in the Ptolemaic system. Claudius Ptolemy was an astronomer in 130 I AD. at the Library and Museum of Alexandria in Alexandria. (Newton, R. R., i The Crime Of Claudius Ptolemy, The John Hopkins University Press, ' Baltimore, 1977) James documented the formation of this Library and Museum of Alexandria from the stolen libraries of the African University Mystery System of Kemit, the Educational Academy that existed for over 4,000 years prior to the Greek occupation of Egypt in 332 B. C. and later Roman occupation in 30 B. C. Accordingly, it appears that Pryse's model is based upon the model of Ptolmey whose Greco-Roman model contained fragments from books by ancient Kemetic African Seers (Grades 2,3). (Kuhn, A. B., Who Is This King Of Glory, A Critical Study of the Chritos-Messiah Tradition, Academy Press, Elizabeth, New Jersey, pp. 357-275, 1944) IN THE ORIGINAL AND KEMETIC PARENT OF PTOLEMY'S MODEL (BIBLE, REV. 1-22) THE SERVICE OF MELANIN IN THE PSYCHIC WORLD AND THE SPIRTUAL WORLD IS BY THE FLOW OF ELECTRONS THROUGH MELANIN DOORS.

According to Bulkey (Bulkey, D. H., An electromagnetic theory of life, Medical hypothe is, 30: pp. 281-285) many events of Living Form cannot be explained by just the paradigm "Life-as-Chemistry." Bulkey said, "some of the failings of the current chemical model should be listed by way of showing a possible need for a Life-as-Physics paradigm. Chemistry is based on "reactions' which involve the discrete transfers of electrons between donors and acceptors. To create large molecules requires a long series of reactions. With physics, on the other hand, there can be flows of electrons as currents with intrinsic magnetic fields Accordingly, an electromagnetic theory of life can be stated in one sentence with five elements: (1) the ultrastructures of life are clearly electromagnetic; (2) the malTomolecules are electrically conductive; (3) with loop closure of long-chain, series linked, high dipole monomers comes "enzyme"-type catalytic activation; (4) with "currents" in (non-resistive?) circuits come toroidal and solenoidal magnetic field..; and (5) with the fields come attractive and repulsive forces to generate replications and motitlities." ...With the advent of the electron microscope we see a fine ultrastructure which could be considered blatantly "electromagnetic" ..Instead of "protplasm' we see a dense matrix of fine filaments and microtubules which are membrae-connected. They in turn consist of coils and coiled coils, dense circuits of fine helical filaments."

Devreotes (Devreotes, P. N., G Protein-Linked Signaling Pathways Control the Developmental Program of Dictyostelim, Neuron 12: p. 235-241, 1994) reported, "The actions of a wide variety of neurotransmitters are mediated by seven transmembrame helix (coil) receptors. .the receptors for (MELANIN=) serotonin (pineal melatonin), dopamine, acetycholine, odorants, and light. ..there is a novel pathway. ..Cainflux. ..by which seven transmembrame helix receptros can transduce signals."

MELANIN IS AT ROOM TEMPERATURE A SEMICON-DUCTOR/SUPERCONDUCTOR TRANSPHYSICAL DOOR FOR THE FLOW OF ELECTRONS. (Cope, F. W., Organic superconductive phenomena at room temperature, Some magnetic properties of dyes and graphite interpreted as manifestations of viscous magnetic flux lattices and small super conductive regions, Physiological Chemistry and Physics, 13: pp. 99-110,1981; Bynum, E. B., Transcending Psychoneurotic Disturbances: New Approaches in Psychospirituality and Personal Development, Harworth Press, Inc., New York, 1994)

MELANIN, "THE EPIDERMAL MELANIN UNIT" AS A NEURAL NETWORK ANALOG COMPUTER

A STUDY OF ANCIENT AFRICAN HISTORY REVEALS THE AFRICAN DEFINITION OF THE HUMAN MELANIN SYSTEM AS A (WHOLE) HOLY BODY BLACK (HBB) THAT SERVES AS THE EYE OF THE SOUL TO PRODUCE INNER VISION, TRUE SPIRITUAL CONSCIOUSNESS, CREATIVE GENIUS, BEATIFIC VISION, TO BECOME GODUKE, AND TO HAVE CONVERSATION WITH THE IMMORTALS (ANCESTORS). THE PURPOSE OF ANCIENT AFRICAN EDUCATION WAS TO PROVIDE THE KNOWLEDGE AND DEVELOPMENT OF THE WILL OF THE STUDENT THAT ALLOWED SALVATION (FREEDOM OF THE SOUL) FROM THE FETTERS (CHAINS) OF THE PHYSICAL BODY. (George James, Stolen Legacy, Chapter 3, U. B. & U. S. Comm. Sys., Inc.) MELANIN IS THE CHEMICAL OF LIFE, THE CHEMICAL OF THE SOUL, A TRANSPHYSICAL DOORWAY THROUGH WHICH THE ENERGY WAVES OF THE HOLY SOUL, SPIRIT, AND MIND PASS TO TAKE FORM AS THE HOLY BODY.

Malavor Ukodari has written (Ukodari, M., The personal ascension of the five senses, Uraeus, 1, (3); 10-14,53,1978; Bailey, A. A., A treatise on cosmic fire, V. 1 and ll, Lcis Publishing Company, New York, 1925), "This transformation, salvation, freedom of the soul) is symbolic of an initiation, i.e., the raising of the lower qualities of the personality in the interest of the higher. It is a spiritual process which takes place in the soul by slow degrees just as evolution proceeds on the lower planes.

Transformation (salvation, freedom of the soul) of the personality or five senses-hearing, sight, smell, taste and touch-is symbolic of the soul's five means of perception on this lesser level which corresponds with the five elementals-earth, water, air, fire, ether-and the five planes (l) physical, (2) astral, (3) mental, (4) buddhic, (5) atmic.

The organs of action which produce karma are: mental action (ears, sound, speech); mental discipline (hands, touch, sensation);

understanding (feet, smell); riddance of lower qualities (taste, mouth, anus, excretion); and production of the higher qualities (generation, third eye, pineal gland).

The five sense organs are symbols of consciousness being transmuted. Hearing on the physical plane becomes "clairaudence" on the astral plane and gives Man an idea of relative direction enabling him to fix his relative direction in the scheme and to locate himself. hearing becomes "higher clairaudence" on the mental plane, "comprehension" on the buddhic plane and "beatitude" on the atmic plane.

Sight on the physical plane becomes "clairvoyance" on the astral plane, and gives Man that mystical vision which enables him to perceive visions from the higher self as it attempts to communicate ideas to the waking conscious mind. Sight becomes "higher claiIVoyance" on the mental plane, "divine vision" on the buddhic plane, and "realization" on the atmic plane.

Smell on the physical plane becomes "emotional idealism" on the astral plane and gives man an idea of the innate qualities enabling him to find that which appeals to him as of the same quality or essence as himself. Smell becomes "spiritual discernment" on the mental plane, "idealism" on the buddhic plane " all knowledge" on the atmic plane.

Taste on the physical plane becomes "imagination" on the astral plane, giving Man an idea of value and enabling him to fix upon that which to him appears best. On the mental plane taste becomes "discrimination", "intuition" on the buddhic plane, and "perfection" on the atomic plane.

Touch on the physical plane becomes "psychometry" on the astral plane and enables Man to measure the soul of something through touching. It becomes "planetary psychometry' on the mental plane, " healing" on the buddhic plane, and "active service" on the atmic plane.

Sensory transformation must be mastered and absorbed into the quality of the soul to attain full expression of the Self."

A. G. E. Pearse (Pearse, A. G. E., Neuroendocrine embryology and the APUD concept, Clinical Endocrinology, 1976; Pearse. A. G. E.. The cytochemsitry and ultrastructure of polypeptide hormone-producing implications for the concept, The Journal of historchemsitry and Cytochemsitry, 17 (5): pp. 303-313, 1969) discovered that many glands function as unified group, the APUD group, which includes the melanocytes, pineal, pituitary, adrenal, mast cells, hypothalamus, thyroid, parathyroid, pant.Teas and many other glands found in the stomach, intestines, lungs, and urogenital tract (Welbourn, Ro B., current status of the apudmoas, Annals of Surgery, 185: pp. 1-12, 1977). Pearse said, "The APUD cells derive their name from the initial letters of their three and most important properties, namely: (1) a high content of Amine, (2) the capacity for Amine Precursor Uptake, and (3) the presence of Amino Acid Decarboxylase for conversion of the amino acid percursor to amine." The amines involved are the chemicals dopamine, norepinephrine, tryptamine, and epinephrine, all precursors of melanin.

THE APUD SERIES OF GLANDS ARE THE GLANDULAR TREE OF THE HOLY BODY BLACK (HBB) AND OPERATE AS A HIGHLY INTERCONNECTED UNIFIED GLANDULAR SYSTEM. In fact all of these glands originate in early pre-fetal life from the neural crest/nerual tube which itself is formed as an invagination of the Melanin containing Black ectoderm skin of the morula/balstula (Morula-Mulberry [Black Berry]) ball of cells formed within hours following fertilization of the female egg by the male sperm in the fallopian tubes. After three days the morula, balstula moves into the Womb (Black Dot, Uterus) to further develop into the fetus/child. The first two hormones produced by the pre-fetus morula/blastula/gastrula after anchoring into the wall of the uterus are HCG and MSH (Meanoccyte Stuimulating Hormone). Melanin is produced throughout life with increased amounts of neuromelanin in the adult years. Melanin serves a critical role in the regeneration of the human form in the process of freedom of the soul that then energizes the transformation/regeneration of the body into a new body with extrasensory Inner Vision of all sensory organs.

MELANIN AND THE 32ND OF THE 42ND KEMETIC NEGATIVE CONFESSION

A STUDY OF ANCIENT AFRICAN HISTORY REVEALS THE AFRICAN DEFINITION OF THE HUMAN MELANIN SYSTEM AS A (WHOLE) HOLY BODY BLACK (HBB) THAT SERVES AS THE EYE OF THE SOUL TO PRODUCE INNER VISION, TRUE SPIRITUAL CONSCIOUSNESS, CREATIVE GENIUS, BEATIFIC VISION, TO BECOME GODLIKE, AND TO HAVE CONVERSATION WITH THE IMMORTALS (ANCESTORS). THE PURPOSE, CONSCIOUSNESS, CREATIVE GENIUS, BEATIFIC VISION, TO BECOME GODLIKE, AND TO HAVE CONVERSATION WITH THE IMMORTALS (ANCESTORS). THE PURPOSE OF ANCIENT AFRICAN EDUCAITON WAS TO PROVIDE THE KNOWLEDGE (ENERGY RECEPTOR) AND DEVELOPMENT OF THE WILL (ENERGY DONOR) OF THE STUDENT THAT ALLOWED SALVATION (FREEDOM) OF THE SOUL (ENERGY, ELECTRON, BLACK DOT) FROM THE FETTERS (CHAINS) OF THE PHYSICAL BODY. (George James, Stolen Legacy, Chapter 3, U. B. & U. S. C. S., Inc.) MEI.ANIN IS THE CHEMICAL OF THE HBB, A KEY TO THE SOUL, A SUPERCONDUCTOR OF DYNAMIC TURNOVER AS A MUSICAL CHOIR, A TRANSPHYSICAL DOORWAY THROUGH WHICH PASS THE ENERGY WAVES O F THE HO L Y SOUL, SPIRIT, AND MIND TO TAKE FORM AS THE HOLY BLACK BODY. MELANIN IS A SEMICONDUTOR/SUPERCONDUCTOR FOR THE FLOW OF ELECTRONS AT ROOM TEMPERATURE. (Bulkey D. H., An electromagnetic theory of life, Medical Hypothesis, 3: pp. 281-285, 1080; Cope, F. W., Organic superconductive phenomena at room temperature, Some magnetic phenomena at room temperature, Some magnetic properties of dyes and graphite interpreted as manisfestations of viscous magnetic flux lattices and small superconductive regions, Physiological Chemistry and Physics, 13: pp. 99-110,1981)

Nur Ankh Amen has written (Nur Ankh Amen, The Ankh, African Origin of Electromagnetism, Nur Ankh Amen Co., Jamainca,

New York, pp. 29, 1993) "Melanin granules (melanosomes) act like tiny primitive eyes, forming a large neural network structure, whose function is to absorb and decode electromeagnetic waves. Neural-network computers are learning machines which are made with a number of receptors that can adjust their weights (quantitative properties) to produce a specific output.

The body of Africans contain massive amounts of melanocytes that encode all life experience in their melanin production, with the aim of creating an actual-reality state after death. During life, visions appear frequently and ESP is common. ..

As semiconductor, melanin has an energy gap. The absorption of energy is required before electrons can jump into the conduction band and make melanin conducting. An increase in conductivity increases the sensitivity of melanin to the electromagnetic world of etheric beings, astral projections and spiritual entities."

Slominski has reported (Slominski, *A.,* Paus, R., Schandendorf, D., Melanocytes as "Sensory" and Regulatory Cells in the Epidemis, J. theor. Biol. 164: pp. 103-120, 1993) "From their strategic location in the basal layer of the epidermis, Melanlocytes (MC) comm\Jnicate via dendritic processes with 36-40 keratincytes (KC, skin cells) to whom they transfer melanin-containing melanosomes. It is generally assumed that the main purpose of this process within the "epidermal melanin unit" is the protection of the keratinocyte DNA from damage by UV-radiation and certain toxins like free oxygen radicals. The color of skin hair also sends important signals of social communication and clmtributes to sexual contact within species. In addition melanized MC may transform the electromagnetic energy of UV light into intracellular chemical messengers and melanin may have thermoregulatory properties by enhancing the absorption of solar light. ..MC operate in the context of one functional epidermal unit, the "epidermal tripod" MC-KC-LC (Langerhans cell, insulin production, shifts between fasting fat metabolism and sugar [carbohydrates] metabolism) ...considering the significance of calcium for regulating the differentiative or proliferative state of keratinocytes as well as epidermal barrier functions MC activities associated with changes in the intracellular calcium concentration in KC deserve special attention. ..the main component of the melanonsome, melanin, furthermore might act as an amorphous semiconductor with potential membrane polarizing capacity relevant to ion permeability. It is particularly important that the heteropolymer melanin is an effective scavenger of oxygen and toxic free radicals. Higher forms of life are trapped in the dilemma of their oxygen-dependence on the one hand and the serious cellular damage caused by continuous exposure to single-electron oxygen on the other. .The transfer of the melanosomes *to* :KC, in summary likely affects multiple KC functions. "THE CONCEPT IS CONFIRMED THAT THE "EPDIERMAL MELANIN UNIT" (MC-KC-LC/MELANOSOMES) DOES SERVE AS A NERUAL NETWORK COMPUTER AS A UNIT AND AS A UNIFIED SYSTEM OF HIGHLY INTERCONNECTED UNITS, THE WHOLE BODY BLACK MELANIN SYSTEM.

On the wall of the tomb of the Kemetic pharaoh Ramses VI are inscriptions of the THE BOOK OF WHAT IS IN THE NETHER-WORLD, TENTH DIVISION, INTRODUCTORY TEXT,

"This Great God (Sun God ra, Light) rests for a while in this cavern. he gives orders to the gods therein. The name of the Gate of this city, by which this Great God enters, is great of Beings, She who gives birth to the forms.

The name of this city Se whose water is deep, whose banks are high.

The name of the Hour of the Night who lead.; this Great God along the mysterious ways of this city who slashes, who decapitates the rebels.

The mysterious Cavern of the West, where Khepri alights in the presence of Re, She who convokes the gods, the spirits, and the dead toward her on the mysterious images of the Region of Silence. This done according to this image which is depicted in the East of the Hidden Chamber of the Netherworld. He who knows them by name will betake himself to the netherworld in order to pass through it. He will be one who cannot be kept from ...the presence of Re." (Pinakoff, A., the Tomb of Ramses VI, Bulligen series XL.I, Pantheon Books, pp. 299-300, 1954)

MELANIN AND THE LIVER, BLOOD AND LYMPHATIC SYSTEMS

A STUDY OF ANCIENT AFRICAN HISTORY REVEALS THE AFRICAN DEFINITION OF THE HUMAN MELANIN SYSTEM AS A (WHOLE) HOLY BLACK BODY (HBB) THAT SERVFS AS THE EYE OF THE SOUL TO PRODUCE INNER VISION, TRUE SPIRTUAL CONSCIOUSNESS, CREATIVE GENIUS, BEATIFIC VISION, TO BECOME GODLIKE, AND TO HAVE CONVERSATION WITH THE IMMORTALS (ANCESTORS). THE PURPOSE OF ANCIENT AFRICAN EDUCATION WAS TO PROVIDE THE KNOWLEDGE AND DEVELOPMENT OF THE WILL OF THE STUDENT THAT ALLOWED SALVATION (FREEDOM OF THE SOUL) FROM THE FETTERS (CHAINS) OF THE PHYSICAL BODY. (George James, Stolen Legacy, Chapter 3, U. B. & U."S. Communications Systems, Inc.)

Please consider the 32nd of 42 Negative Confessions of Ancient Kemet, "Hail. Serekhi, coming forth from Unth, I have not. ..my skin, I have not ...the god." (Budge, E. A. W., Osiris, The Egyptian Religion of Resurrection. University Books, New Hyde Park, New York. pp. 342,1961) The importance of skin was so important to Kamites, whose skin was Black from high levels of eumelanin, that the proper treatment of the skin was specifically listed as one of the 42 Negative Confessions for development of the Heart, Will, and Right Cortical Consciousness. Dr .Patricia (Sekmet) Newton in a public communication (Baltimore, Maryland, 1994) has offered the interpretation, "I have not BLEACHED my skin."

Piankoff has noted (Piankoff, *A.,* The Tomb of Ramses VI, Bolingen series, SLI, Pantheon Books, pp. 37,1954)," During the day, in the sky above, the sun god called Re or Horus of the Horizon, being represented as a hawk-headed man. In the sky below, in the region of the night, he is the god of the setting and dead sun, Atum or the Flesh of Re (Sunlight energy now passed through Melanin superconductor doorways as a flow of electrons to donors/receptors throughout the (Whole) Holy Black Body Melanin System (HBB), Pineal Melatonin is released in rhythmic patterns during the Night to play the HBB Melanin Harp as a Musical Choir of Dynamic Turnover (Dreams, Trance States), personified as a man with the head of a ram. He will be born again as Khepri. the Becoming One, the visible sun on the eastern horizon at sunrise-symbolized by a scarab bet tie carrying disk."

According to Bulkey (Bulkey, D. H., An electromagnetic theory of life, Medical Hypothesis, 30: pp. 281-285,1989) in an electromagnetic theory of life the structures of life are clearly electromagnetic (coils) with "currents" in (non-resisitive?) (semiconductor/superconductor circuits come toroidal and solenoidal magnetic fields and with the fields come attractive (positive, negative-negative, male-male, female-female) to generate replications (self-meaning, self-conquest/self-transformation, salvation), top of the spinal (Djed) Column) (Divine sexual reproduction, bottom of the spinal (Djed) column) and motilities (movement, rhythmic patterns that translate various forms of energy flows of electrons into the choir music (resonant harmonics of sound waves) of a dynamic turnover of flows of electrons. Consider the symbolic analogy (similar function (Color , sound, taste, smell) though different structure) of what Dereotes has written (G-Protein-linked Signaling Pathways Control the Developmental Program of Dictyostelium, Neuroan 12: pp. 235-241, 1994)," As the multicellular structure undergoes morphogenesis, forming a migrating slug and ultimately a fruiting body, cells in the anterior or posterior regions of these structures, under the continued influence of CAMP, differentiate into stalk or spore cells." All of this is to say that a coil structure of African hair may be critical for magnetic field signal transduction of light and communication of the Melanin transformed five sensory organs of the saved (free) Holy (Whole-WBBMS) Soul.

Ortonne and Prota have written (Ortonne, J., Prota, G., Hair Melanin and Hair Color: Ultrastructual and Biochemical Aspects, J. Invest. Dermatol. 101: 825-895, 1993)," The pigmentation of hair follicle follows a sequence of events identical to those seen in the epidermis. The color of the hair is based on the pigment content of the hair shaft. By analogy of the epidemal melanin unit. the pigmentation of hair is regulated by these follicular melanin unit (neural net work analog computer). ..two categories of melanin pigments. How can one interpret the biologic complexity illustrated by the wide range of colors of mammalian hair, including human hair ranging through shades of yellow, orange, and red as well as black, grey, and white? ...Human Blond Hairs. ..Melanin granules are smaller and less numerous than in dark-haired subjects. Melanosomes are not fully melanized even in the dendritic processes of melaocytes. This suggests that the light color in blond hair may be due to quantitative decrease in the production and melanization of melanosomes. Human Black and Brown Hairs: Typical ellipsoidal melanosomes, at various stages of melanization, are observed in follicular mealocytes of black hair. Their ultrastructural characteristics are identical to those seen in the epidermis or caucasoids and negroids. Melanosomes transferred to neighboring keratinocytes are singly distributed. In brown hair, the follicular melanocytes also contain all the developmental stages of eumelanosomes. Lighter brown hairs have smaller melanosomess.

MELANIN AND THE KEMETIC STUDY OF ELECTROMAGNETISM, ELEKTRON, THEHENT, AMBER AND CRYSTAL

A STUDY OF ANCIENT AFRICAN HISTORY REVEALS THE AFRICAN DEFINITION OF THE HUMAN MELANIN SYSTEM AS A (WHOLE) HOLY BLACKBODY (HBB) THAT SERVES AS THE EYE OF THE SOUL TO PRODUCE INNER VISION. THE PURPOSE OF ANCIENT AFRICAN EDUCATION WAS TO PROVIDE THE KNOWLEDGE (ENERGY RECEPTORS) AND DEVELOPMENT OF THE WILL (ENERGY DONORS) OF THE STUDENT THAT ALLOWED SALVATION (FREEDOM, MOTILITY, HARMONIC RESONANCE) OF THE HOLY (WHOLE) (ENERGY, ELECTRON FLOW, BLACK DOT, MICRO BLACK HOLE) FROM THE FETTERS (CHAINS, DISHARMONIC NONRESONANCE) OF THE HOLY (WHOLE) PHYSICAL BODY. (George James, *Stolen Legacy,* Chapter 3, U. B. & U. S. C. S., Inc.)

IN AN ELECTROMAGNETIC THEORY OF LIFE (Bulkey, D. H., An Electromagnetic theory of life, Medical Hypothesis, 30: pp. 281-285, 1989) THE STRUCTURES OF LIFE ARE CLEARLY ELECTROMAGNETIC WITH "CURRENTS" IN (NON-RESISTIVE?, SEMICONDUCTOR, SUPERCONDUCTOR) CIRCUITS COME TOROIDAL AND SOLENOIDAL MAGNETIC FIELDS AND WITH FIELDS COME ATTRACTIVE AND .REPULSIVE GENERATE REPLICATIONS (SELF MEANING, I AM, SELF TRANSFORMATION, BEING THE ANGEL) AND MOTILITY (HARMONIC RESONANCE, UNITY WITH LIGHT, CONVERSATION WITH THE IMMORTALS).

PLEASE CONSIDER THE SYMBOLIC ANALOGY OF THE OBSERVATION THAT WHILE IN A FASTING STATE (LACK OF DENSE PHYSICAL MATTER FOOD. USE OF ENVIRONMENTAL LIGHT AND INTERNAL LIGHT FROM ETERNAL INTERNAL SUN) AS THE MULTICELLULAR STRUCTURE UNDERGOES (EPIGENESIS?, FORMATION OF NEW STRUCTURES FROM AN UNDEVELOPED STATE THROUGH

THE INFLUENCE OF THE HIGHLY DEVELOPED END STAGE
FORM) MORPHOGENESIS (FORMATION AND GENERATION
OF TISSUES AND ORGANS), THERE WAS FORMED A
MIGRATING SLUG AND ULTIMA TEL Y A FRUITING BODY,
CELLS IN THE ANTERIOR OR POSTERIOR REGIONS OF
THESE STRUCTURES UNDER THE CONTINUED INFLUENCE
OF CAMP (MESSENGER ANGEUC EQUVALENT , MELANIN
ANALOG, ENERGY RECEPTION), DIFFERENTIATE INTO
STALK (COLUMN, SEMI- CONDUCTOR/SUPERCONDUCTOR
ELECTRON FLOW CIRCUIT, SOLENOIDAL(CYLINDER
SHAPED) MAGNETIC FIELD, MOTILITY) OR SPORE CELLS
(SELF REPLICATION, SELF TRANSFORMATION, SAIAVA-
TION (FREEDOM OF THE ANGEL), ENERGY DONATION,
TOROIDAL (DOUGHNUT SHAPED) MAGNETIC FIELD)
(Dereotes, G- Protein-Linked Signaling Pathways Control the
Developmental Program of Dictyostelum, Neuron 12: pp. 235-
241,1994).

Dichel has noted (Sichel, G., Biosynthesis and Function of
Melanins in Hepatic Pigmentary System, Pigment Cell Research 1:
pp. 250-258, 1988), Contrary to the cutaneous pigment cells that
derive from the neural (.Test, the liver pigment cells, instead derive
from Kuppner cells. ..amphibia and reptilia Kuppner cells are able to
synthesize melanin themselves. ..liver pigment cells of Arnphibia and
Reptilia should be classified as "Extra Cutaneous Pigment Cells from
Histocytic (Blood) Origin". ..As regards the function of the melanins,
we show that O2 is trapped by these substances, oxide dismutase
activity is inversely proportional to the quantity of melanin present;
thus, we think that melanin could mime SOD activity. ..the basic life
phenomena appear as methods devised in order to protect living matter against oxygen, and this operation is actualized by elegant enzy-
matic systems (progression of resonant harmonic magnetic fields),
as, for example, SOD catlases, peroxidases and so on, I think it is
very probable that these systems, during phylogenesis, have been
formed relatively recently and that formerly, when the reducer atmosphere became an oxidant one, this function was performed by simpler
molecules than the ezymatic ones, such as catecholamines and
melanin."

This is a major observation that links the role of melanin in living systems to the evolution of O2/CO2 in the atmosphere of planetary bodies in which the formation of a planetary atmosphere experiences change in the oxygen/carbon dioxide balance as a result of geological forces that release oxygen from minerals, generation of oxygen by plants and carbon dioxide by animals, chlorophyll pigment reception of light in plants, melanin reception of light in animals, and the epigenetic/morophogenetic changes in form of plants and animals in the planetary biosphere in relationship to the earth's geomagnetic field to the sun and solar system planetary magnetic fields as the solar system, magnetic fields of nearby stars as the sun orbits the center of our Milky Way Galaxy and magnetic field relationships with other Galaxies in this expression of the universe. There is melanin in interstellar gas clouds of galaxies, Cosmic Melanin.

Wasserman has reported (Wassermann, H.P., Melanokinetics and the biological significance of melanin, The British Journal of Dermatology, 82 (5): pp. 530-534, 1970), the vascular transport of melanin in blood and lymphatic circulation of humans. Lymphocytes, acquiring melanin in the inflammatory response. ..circulate in the "fourth circulation" and re-enter the circulation via Iymthatics. An examination of leukocyte concentrate from the pheriperal blood of normal Bantu revealed pigmented mononuclear cells. Lymph nodes draining skin more often contain melanin than do abdominal lymph nodes. Melanin is found in about 75% of similar nodes in Bantu."

Considering the stated role of melanin as a receptor for free radicals such as oxygen, which is transported by blood cells in blood throughout the body there is considerable importance for a melanin presence in white blood cells in the vascular tree. Then too, there is the service of melanin as a carrier of metals, protein carrier molecules, bound charged molecules and ions as a energetic entity itself within the vascular tree as a circuit to toroidal and solenoidal magnetic fields. The vascular tree may be a freeway for the Blood Bourne Motile Melanin Computer, The Melanin-White Blood Cell-Red Blood Cell Neural Net Work. Analog Computer. Again, there is a (Whole) Holy Black Body Melanin System that is highly interconnected.

MELANIN AND OXYGEN IN COSMIC, PLANETARY, AND PLANT/ANIMAL EVOLUTION

A STUDY OF ANCIENT AFRICAN HISTORY REVEALS THE AFRICAN DEFINITION OF THE HUMAN MELANIN SYSTEM AS A (WHOLE) HOLY BLACK BODY (HBB) THAT SERVES AS THE EYE OF THE SOUL TO PRODUCE INNER VISION, TRUE SPIRITUAL CONSCIOUSNESS, CREATIVE GENIUS, BEATIFIC VISION, TO BECOME GODLIKE, AND TO HAVE CONVERSATION WITH THE IMMORTALS (ANCESTORS). THE PURPOSE OF ANCIENT AFRICAN EDUCATION WAS TO PROVIDE THE KNOWLEDGE AND DEVELOPMENT OF THE WILL OF THE STUDENT THAT ALLOWED SALVATION (FREEDOM OF THE SOUL) FROM THE FETTERS (CHAINS) OF THE PHYSICAL BODY. (George James, Stolen Legacy, Chapter 3, U. B. & U. S. Communications Systems, Inc.)

FROM THE ORIGINAL KEMETIC PARENT MODEL OF THE UNIVERSE WAS LATER PRODUCED THE BIBLICAL MODEL OF THE APOCALYPSE, REV. 1-22 (APOKALYPSIS (UNCOVERING, UNVEILING), EPOPTEIA (BEHOLDING, FACING GOD)=INITIATION INTO THE GREATER MYSTERIES) THE SERVICE OF MELANIN IN THE PHYSICAL WORLD AND SPIRITUAL WORLD IS BY THE FLOW OF ELECTRONS THROUGH MELANIN DOORS. (Kuhn, A. B., Who Is This King Of Glory, A Critical Study of the Christos-Messiah Tradition, Academy Press, Elizabeth, N. J., pp. 257-275,1944; Psyse, JM., Apocalypse Unsealed, (the drama of self conquest), Health Research, Mokelumne Hill, California, pp. 68,33-75,1965.

The word electron is from the Greek word elektron which was the Greek name for amber. The Kemetic name for amber is thehent which is the same name for both amber and crystal. This is evidence of the Kemetic study of the electron (electronics). When a crystal is placed under pressure it produces a now of elelctrons, pizeoelectric effect, just as amber produces a flow of electrons when rubbed against wool, electrical current. (Budge, E. A. W., A. Hieroglyphic Vocabulary To the Book Of The Dead, Dover Publications, N. Y ., pp. 453-, 1991).

MELANIN IS A SEMICONDUCTOR/SUPERCONDUCTOR FOR THE FLOW OF ELECTRONS AT ROOM TEMPERATURE. (Bulkey, D. IH., An electronmagnetic theory of life, Medical Hypothesis, 3: pp. 281-285, 1989; Jacobson, J. I., "Exploring The Potential Of Magneto-Recrystallization Of Genes And Associated Structures With Respect To Nerve Regeneration And Cancer," Intern. J. Neuroscience, 64: pp. 153-165, 1992; Nur Ankh Amen, The Ankh, African Origin of Electromagnetism, Nur Ankh Amen Co., Jamaica, N. Y., 1993).

On the wall of the tomb of the Kemetic Pharoah Ramses VI, are inscriptions of the BOOK OF THE GATES, Tenth Division, Name of the gate: The Holy One; In the barge of Re (Type of energy flow): are (1) The Flesh of Re (The Face of Sun god Ra shown as the Face of a Black Man with Gray Coiled Hair, Full Nose, Full Lips, and Jet Black Skin), (2) Magic (will), (3) Mind (knowledge memory), and (4) The Enveloper (time). ..Text on the door: He is upon this door, he opens fl)f Re. Mind (says to) the Uniter (serpent, association of events by similar sensory qualities): Open thy Netherworld (subconscious, superconscious, collective unconscious) for RE (light), throw open thy door (Whole Body Black Melanin System, the seven helix (coil) transmembrame receptor, melanin mediated neurotransmitters for brain pathway signal transduction). He lightens the complete darkness and makes) the Hidden Chamber (Skull? , Pineal/Pituitary mediated Third Ventricle) bright. (ENERGY RECEPTORS?) =Upper Uraeus: She who lights for Re. Lower Uraeus: She who lights for Re. (ENERGY DONORS?)=Upper Guardian: The Executioner. He bends his arm before Re. Lower Guardian: The Uncoverer. he bends his arm before Re. (Pianfoff, A., The Tomb of Rarnses VI, Bolligen series XL. 1, Pantheon Books, Plate 58, pp. 203-208, 1954) It appears that this Ancient African University Text of the Tenth Gate of the book of the Gates defines the effect of Sunlight Upon skin melanin (Flesh of Re) of the head and face in the development of Mind, Magic (Will), and the student's use of Time. There can be no question as to the African phrase," the flesh of Re," as Re is clearly shown in the face-on view of the head and neck of a Black Skin Black Man. Sunlight passing through the Melanin Flesh of Re of the head and neck makes active melanin whole body pathways that brighten dark chambers symbolically and literally.

Richard Frenkel has written (Frenkel, R., Overcoming Stress, Richardson and Steirman, Inc., New York) that the mind (brain) stores experiences in their respective colors. He observed that when patients are exposed to particular colors painful memories return, often accompanied with bodily symptoms associated with the original experiences. His treatment consisted of the daily wearing of glasses tinted to the same color that evoked the pain which desensitized and optically negated the color's link to the painful memories and bodily symptoms. Jacob Liberman has reviewed (Liberman, J., Light Medicine Of The Future, Bear & Cimpany, Santa Fe, New Mexico, 1991) the use of light in the treatment of various forms of illness -Sharon McDonald's use of blue light for pain relief from rhumatoid arthritis; John Anderson's use of red light to stop or decrease migraine headaches; Harry Wohlfarth's use of full-spectrum lighting and wall colors of bright warm colors such as yellow and orange to improve the academic achievement of school-age children. Sunlight therapy has been used to help patients with tuberculosis, colitis, anemia, gout, cystitis, arterioscleosis, eczema, acne, herpes, lupus, sciatica, asthma some forms of kidney disease, and burns. Liberman reported the use of UV light to increase Calcium absorption, lower blood pressure, increase the efficiency of the heart, improve the EKG and blood profiles (cerebral circulation) of patients with arterisclerosis, reduce cholesterol, increase weight loss; and increase the level of sex hormones.

Melanin in the living universe exists on at least five different planes. These planes are the cosmic, planetary, vegetable, animal, and "saved" human (transformed) human, higher mental, genius, "homo maximus").

Considering cosmic melanin, there exists complex organic molecules in vast interstellar gas clouds that are literally many light years (millions of millions of mile..') in size as found at the central disc regions of our Milky Way galaxy and in many other galaxies in the universe. The central atom in such organic molecule...' is the carbon atom, the central atom of melanin. The carbon atom is formed in the center of most main sequence stars as they evolve. At a certain phase of main sequence star development there comes a star eruption (birth?) in which the star sheds its accumulated carbon into the surrounding space to later combine with other molecules to form complex organic molecules.

Critically, as the star and planetary families such as our solar system rotate around the center of our galaxy, every several hundred thousand years, our solar system just as other solar systems will pass through this black carbon, Complex organic molecule, melanin interstellar gas cloud. Upon doing so the Cometary frozen balls of ice that comprise the Orht cloud that surround the solar system is literally bathed in Black melanin. Accordingly, at some distant later time occasional comets from the solar system outer regions will pass into the inner regions and will partially melt upon exposure to the sun's radiation. Upon doing so, the Comet leaves in space a trail of complex organic molecules/melanin that will seed planetary surfaces as the planet eventually passes through the trails of Comets.

Complex organic molecules in the form of Melanin are found in the Vegetable Kingdom as the class of photopigments known as chlorophyll. Chlorophyll appears as a green colored pigment that serves to hold and transform light into a chemical bond that can be utilized by the plant for fuel to energize various cellular operations.

Whereas in the Animal Kingdom melanin exists as a similar class of photopigments to hold or transform light into a chemical bond that can be utilized by the animal for fuel to energize various cellular operations.

Additionally, in human animals, melanin systems can be shown to process the transformation of energy from chemical bonds back into various forms of light in discrete informationally significant packets to thereby shape and organize physical matter. This is the first form of melanin operation in animals, homo maximus, that have been elevated to the "spiritually saved" level in which one can communicate with the immortals and use dreams and visions to shape one's conduct and organize the physical world into the actual form seen in one's dreams.

There are levels beyond those of the higher mental such as the Buddhic, and Atmic levels. It is presently unknown as to what role is served by melanin on these levels. However, there is a vast vision of possible relationships if one considers the cosmic perspective of stellar carbon and the possibility of spiritual intellects of stellar and galactic dimensions.

MELANIN AND SEXUAL ENERGY, DIVINE CREATIVE ENERGY

A STUDY OF ANCIENT AFRICAN HISTORY REVEALS THE AFRICAN DEFINITION OF THE HUMAN MELANIN SYSTEM AS A WHOLE BODY BLACK MELANIN SYSTEM THAT SERVES AS THE EYE OF THE SOUL TO PRODUCE INNER VISION, TRUE SPIRITUAL CONSCIOUSNESS, CREATIVE GENIUS, BEATIFIC VISION, TO BECOME GODLIKE, AND TO HAVE CONVERSATION WITH THE IMMORTALS (ANCESTORS). THE PURPOSE OF ANCIENT AFRICAN EDUCATION WAS TO PROVIDE THE KNOWLEDGE AND DEVELOPMENT OF THE WILL OF THE STUDENT THAT ALLOWED SALVATION (FREEDOM OF THE SOUL) FROM THE FETTERS (CHAINS) OF THE PHYSICAL BODY. (George James, Stolen Legacy, Chapter 3, U. B. & U. S. Communications, Systems, Inc.)

IN AN ELECTROMAGNETIC THEORY OF LIFE (BULKEY, D. H., An Electromagnetic theory of life, Medical Hypothesis, 30: pp. 281-285, 1989) THE STRUCTURES OF LIFE ARE CLEARLY ELECTROMAGNETIC WITH "CURRENTS" IN (NONRESISTIVE? , SEMICONDUCTOR/SUPERDONDUCTOR CIRCUITS COME TOROIDAL AND SOLENOIDAL MAGNETIC FIELDS AND WITH FIELDS COME ATTRACTIVE (SEXUAL) AND RELPULSIVE (FEAR) GENERATE REPLICATION (SELF MEANING, I AM,. SELF TRANSFORMATION, BEING THE ANGEL) AND MOTILITY (HARMONIC RESONANCE, UNITY WITH LIGHT, CONVERSATION WITH THE IMMORTALS).

Dr. John Chissell has written (Chissell, I. T., Pyramids Of Power, An Ancient African Centered Approach Centered To Optimal Health, Positive Perceptions Publications, Baltimore, Maryland, pp. 60, 61, 65, 1993) ..."One of the most frequently overlooked and/or undervalued relationships in our daily lives is the relationship with ourselves. ..always apporach any relationship with respect, especially the relationship with ourselves. Respecting ourselves means positive self talk (saying constructive and encouraging things to ourselves), nonjudgement, and using constructive critique of our daily choices and decisions with a vie toward directing our energy toward our greatest potentials and highest good (self love). ..Think about it; of all of the energies that the Creator had to choose from to make possible the creation of additional human beings, the Creator chose sexual energy. Thus by definition, sexual energy is the original DIVINE CREATIVE ENERGY. Orgasm in this context may be defined as the celebration of meeting with the DIVINE through your sexual partner. ..Optimal economic health is defined as that state of aliveness in which we are constantly aware of, and believe in, the universal law of abundance. The universal law of abundance simply means that the CREATOR has given us everything we need internally and externally, to survive and thrive on this planet if we are willing to earn and accept what is our due. What we are due is adequate food, clothing and shelter, now and every day, to allow us to move toward our greatest potential and highest good as we use our special talents to earn things above and beyond what we need to sustain life in its optimally healthy form."

Similarily Wallis Budge has written (Budge, Wallis, The Gods of the Egyptians, Dover Publications, N. Y., V. 1,1969) "Closely associated with Thoth (Tehuti) in the performance of certain of his duties as the god of letters and learning, was the goddess whose name is generally read Sefthet (Sesheta). ..we see her without her panther skin garmet, holding a writing reed in the right hand, and the cartouche symbolic of "name" in her left; in this form she suggests the idea of being a kind of recording angel, not so much of the deeds committed by man, but of their names, of which she, presumably, took note, that her associate Thoth might declare them before Osiris. In the title which accompanies this picture she is called "great one, lady of letters, mistress of the house of books."

Liberman has recorded (Liberman, J ., Light, Medicine Of The Future, Bear & Company, Sante Fe, New Mexico, pp. 135,1991) "My menses is a time when I experience feeling "low to the ground" (depression, premenstrual syndrome, dysharmony) or "pulled to the Earth." It's as though I am being pulled into its introspective caves-to reflect on how I'm handling my immediate life experiences, now, and to listen to that stillness deep within me. It's a time when, whatever learning processes I'm in, I am enlightened and heightened with emotional (intuition) awareness. ...In some of the Native American cultures, the women's "moon time" visions that the tribal chief received guidance for his people's next move or what they needed to know as a whole ...the shifts that occur during winter and menses (seasonal, daily day/night) are truly meant for cleansing the psyche. .because of this chronic repression, certain times of the day, months, and/or seasons will tend to retrigger these feelings, resulting in anxiety, depression, and general emotional upset (seasonal affective disrorder, depression, anxiety in both males and females)."

Sizonenko and Aubert have written (Sizonenko, P. C. and Aubert, M. L., Neuroendocrine Changes Characteristic of Sexual Maturartion, J. Neural Transm [Suppl] 21: pp. 159-181,1986) "such factors will initiate the activity of the hypothalamus to generate the pulsatile release of GnRh and secondarily the augernnted secretion of gonadotropins and sex steroids (gonardarche). This "oscillator" is under the influence of brain neurotransmitters" (catecholamines and serotonin), endogenous opiate peptides and of probably pineal melatonin." (Eye of Hem, Eye of the Soul, Eye of Inner Vision) The chronic lowering of melatonin secretion levels during ovulation, and low levels at the middle of menses (28 day moon cycle) with similar melatonin levels for male sperm production during the 40 day sun cycle.

GLOSSARY

Absorption-to absorb as in a sponge, interception, adherance, the taking in of radiant energy or sound waves

Accumulator-a storage system.

Acetylcholine-a catecholamine, precursor of Melanin, a compound, released at autonomic nerve endings, a neurotransmitter in certain tracts of neurons in brain. A neurotansmitter of the parasympathetic peripheral autonomic nervous system, that is associated with increased sensitivity for telepathy, increased acetylcholine levels have been linked to a sense of travelling clairvoyance. See p. 19 of Valerian, 1992 and Moller, 1992.

Acne-a skin disorder caused by inflammation of skin sebaceous glands and hair follicles.

A.D.-Anno Domini, in the year of the lord, the Christian Era, said to date from year 1. the year of the birth of "Jesus the Christ". A dating system of years that begins with the year 1 A.D. being 30 years after the Roman conquest of Greek-Ptolemy occupied Kemet. Note, no historical records exist of the actual personality of" Jesus the Christ" although their are Kemetic equivalents in the Kemetic University Third Grade of Son of Light, Hero, and over 30 IIMessiah" (Melanin Transformed, Soul Ascended, Soul "Saved", Soul Free, "god/goddess", Perfected Man/Woman, Homo Maximus) Ideal Human Types in cultures through- out the world. See, Jackson, 1985; Ben-Jochannan, 1970; and Khun 1944, 1949. Note a new book by Rudolph R. Windsor, Judea Trembles, under Rome does provide a definition of Jesus of Galilee.

Adam Kadmon-A term found in the Hebrew Magical System of the Kabbalah, a theory of emanations (projections) of the Godhead as ten sephiroth or intellegences that refer to the Inner "primordial man, homo maximus, archetype of the soul of man, Human collective unconscious memories of the original African ancestors). Please note the critical relationship of the Kabbalah to parent Kemetic philosophical concepts as defined in the Memphite Theology (3,000 B.C +)with the emanation (projection) of the four pairs of Gods from Ptah in a hierarchy of powers and creative processes. The Hebrews had no written theology or science before their residence in Kemit. See Ben-Jochannan, 1970, 1983; Waite; Ponce,1973; Guthrie, 1992; Bradley 1992,1992; Jung,1963,1967; Windsor, 1969, 1994; Kllestler,1976; James, 1988, Piankoff,1954, 1977; Faulkner, 1969, 1978; Emboden, 1989; and Mercier, 1979.

African-Commonly referred to as the Black Man/Black woman, a person of immediate (blood line African parents from after 1492 A.D.) African ancestry. Important visible traits have been linked to various shades of Black skin color with oval Melanosomes, high - moderate Melanin content of the Melanosome, Melanin is of largely Eumelanin type with low (less than 1%) content of Sulphur, frequently with circulating Melanin in white blood cells and melanin present in lymph nodes, high extracutaneous levels of melanin in inner ear, substantia nigra, locus coeruleus, high serum Vitmain D, Parathyroid Hormone, Bone Density, and very importantly high Pineal Gland blood/ C.S.F. Melantonin levels. Profound considerations exist for definitions of Black connsciousness as cited in Kemetic definitions of the Perfect Black as Wosir (Osiris), Black Cubit (Nilometric Cubit), Jet (Black), and the all Black underworld of Arnenta (The Special Place [The Unconscious] and Abode of the the god [Human Soul]), and the relationship of the Mythology of Cinderella, the Story of the Woman Hidden by Black Cinders from the Fireplace (Black Smith Forge) to Isis Veiled or Children born with a Veil over their face. See Ben-Jochannan, 1970; King, 1976; Bayley, 1968; Bell, 1985; Meleski, 1977; Montagana, 1993; Shosuke, 1993; KllCh, 1986; Welsing, 1973, 1990; Andrews,1989; Barnes 1988,1993; Ani,1994; and King, 1990,1991,1992, 1992,1993,1993, 1993,1994.

Albinism-a condition of genetic mutation in which the life form lacks the enzyme tyrosinase in skin Melanocytes and cannot convert the amino acid Tyrosine into various intennediate catecholamine forms such as Dopa and Dopamine that are all precursors to the end/beginning product of Melanin. Critically Melanin can be made in internal oragan sites such as brain neuromelanin by the action of a different enzyme, tyrosine hydroxylase. Albino life forms lack only melanin only in superficial skin cites and do possess large internal organ stores of Melanin. See Tyrosinase, Tyrosinase Hydroxylase, and Oculocutaneous Albinism. See Erickson, 1993; Montagna, 1993; and Nordlund, 1989.

Alchemy-a psychological symbolic process in which from the Black Ore, Khem (Jet), by the use of Quick Silver, Mercury (Mind/ Soul/Spirit) the Gold (Light, Astronomical Influences) and Silver (Emanations, Light Projections into Black Primeveal Waters of Nun [Space]) are perceived, understood and controlled in a rhthymical atonement manner by becoming a "Golden Thread" in the fabric of Creation with a perfect fulfillment of One's Mission in Life by inspired service of Cosmic Be- coming/ Beingness. A Science of Kemetic origin. See Budge 1971; Jung, 1963,1967,1974

Al-khemeia- The Black God. the Arabic name for the Kemetic Process of Khem (Chemistry). Alchemy. the psychospiritual chemical process of Melanin mediated Soul Ascension or Salvation (Freedom of the Soul). See Budge 1971

Al'lah- The name for the supreme God of the Universe in the religion of Islam. See the Holy Qu'ran and Ben-Jochannan, 1970

Al' lat- The Sun Gl1ddess worhsiped in Mecca prior to the time of the Prophet Mohamet. See Ben-Jochannan, 1970.

AI-Manat- The Goddess of Venus worshiped in Mecca prior to the time of the Prophet Mohamet. See Ben-JI.1Channan, 1970.

AI.Uzzah- The Fortune Goddess worshiped in Mecca prior to the time of the Prophet Mohamet. See Ben-Jochannan, 1970.

Amber-A hard translucent fossil resin (plant sap or secretion) of a brown to yellow color, kemetic name being thehent, Greek name being elektron. See Budge, 1991; and Amen, 1993.

Amenta- The Kemetic name for the UndelWorld, Duat, NethelWorld, the Special Place or Abode (Ta) of the God (Amen), also the special place and able of the body fettered Human Soul. See Budge, 1967, 1969, 1971, 1991, Piankoff, 1954, 1957; Faulkner,1968. 1978; and King, 1990.

Amorphous Semiconductor- In regards to Melanin, Melanin is a chemical compound and series of physical events that is amorphous because it is constantly in motion. always changing as a result of its inherent core structure and constant transformation of form/levels of energy into other energetic forms. During the course of such energy translations Melanin displays semiconductor properties by having low resistance to the flow of electrons. Thus Melanin serves as a switch or door to a Melanin Tunnel for the flow of electrons to higher or lower form/levels of energy manisfestation in Nun (Space). See Barnes 1988; Cope, 1981; Crippa,1978; Graham, 1979; Jacobson, 1992; King, 1990,1992, 1- 993,1994; Kono, 1980; Lacy, 1984; McGinness, 1985; Stevens,1974; Strzelecka, 1982; and Valerian, 1992.

Amygala- A mass of grey matter in the anterior portion of the temporal lobe in brain.

Androgynous- Having the nature of both male and female.

Anemia-A disorder in which there is a low number of red blood cells or hemoglobin. the compound that carries, oxygen inside of red blood cells.

Animal Kingdom Melanin- Melanin that is present in Animal Life Forms. Melanin appears to playa critical role in celluar respiration, body stability in heat economy, responses to large scale atmospheric changes in oxygen and carbon dioxide, and of course absorption of radiant Light and conversion into Self-replicating Motile Life Form

Platforms/Systems. See Bulkey, 1989; and Czerakas, 199.1; Sichel, 1988; and Devreotes, 1994.

Antennae-in Humans a helical coil structure device for radiating or receiving energy waves. See Bulkey 1989; Dereotes, 1994; and Ortonne, J. ,1993.

Anterior Fontanelle- The "soft spot" present in the anterior area of the skull of infants, a membranous space at the junction of the coronal, sagittal and metopic sutures where the parietal bones meet the two ununited halves of the frontal skull bones.

Anxiety-A feeling-toned state associated with an increased conscious awareness, the fonn and content of which is determined by both the base- line level of Melanin mediated integration of the Nervous System and H.B.B and level of personal development, accumulation of "good emotions" by "right conduct," The degree of Locus coeruleus Melanin content has been correlated with feelings that range from prudence, watchfulness, attentiveness to terror, panic, fear, or impulsivity, carelessness and recklessness. George James in the book Stolen Legacy defined Prudence, "Evidence of having a mission in life and Evidence of a call to spiritual Orders or the Priesthood in the Mysteries: the combination of which was equivalent to Prudence or a deep insight and graveness that befitted the faculty of Seership." Thus the feeling of Prudence was well known to ancient Kamites as one of the Kemetic 10 Virtues that developed a State of Seership (Melanin mediated sensory organ transformation or metamorphosis, Ascension, Soul Slavation or Freedom of the Soul once the Melanin Key had opened the lock on the chains [fetters] of the physical body that enslaved and kept asleep the Soul [Creative Genius {The Geni}]). See section on Locus Coeruleus [Black Dot] in King, 1990; Valerian, 1992; Bazelon, 1967; Fenichel, 1968; Marsden, 1969;and James, 1988.

Apocalypse-Jewish-Christian writings of 200 B.C. to 150 A.D. in which symbolic imagery of a cosmic catalysm in which God destroys the ruling powers of evil and raises the good to life in heaven. There are in fact earlier Kemetic writings in which God in a cosmic catalysm does destroy evil human and demon entities and preserves the good humans. See Pryce,1965; and Budge, 1912

Apokalpse- the Greek/English spelling of Apocalypse which in Greek means unveiling, facing or iniation. See Pryce, 1965.

Apokalypsis-the Greek/English spelling of Apocalypse which in Greek means unveiling, facing or iniation. See Pryce, 1965.

A.P.U.D. System-A system of endocrine glands that all originate in embrologicallife in the pre fetus from the neural crest derived Melanin containing ectoderm. All glands of this system possess the enzyme, decarboxylase (detaches carbon atoms) and are actively involved in the uptake of amines. This Melanin mediating glandular tree is a critical part of the H.B.B. pineal gland, pituitary, adrenals, gastrointestinal tract glands, urogential tract glands, etc.. See Pearse, 1969, 1976; King, 1990; Eberle, 1988; and Ban, 1983.

Arabla- a peninsula of land that to the west is connected to Africa and on the east is connected to Asia which borders the Red Sea on the west coast, Arabian Sea on the southern coast, and Persian gulf on the eastern
coast.

Area postrema- a section of the brain involved in the pineal honnone melatonin mediated induction of R.E.M. sleep.

Asthersclerosis-A disorder involving the vascular tree in which fat deposits are imbeded in arterial walls and become calcified with hardening of the arteries that then lead to High blood pressure as the heart must pump blood at higher pressures to circulate blood through less elastic arteries. This condition often results in complete blockage of arteries to the heart that results in heart attacks (death of heart muscle from stopage of blood circulation) and strokes (C. V .A., cerebral vascular accidents in which blood vessels to the brain are blocked or break from high blood pressure upon fragile diseased arterial vessel walls. See Liberman, 1991.

Asthma-A disorder in which the airways inside of the lungs become constricted. See Liberman, 1991

Astral Plane-A level of consciousness above the dense material level upon which human exist when out of the body during sleep or loss of a direct electromagnetic linkage to the physical body. See Powell, 1987; Pryce, 1965; Valerian, 1992.

Astral Projection-Conscious control of the projection of consciousness of the astral body and sensory organs into the astral realm and or other dimensions of the physical realm.See Powell, 1987; Pryce, 1965; Valerian, 1992.

Atomic Plane-A level of consciousness above the astral plane, a level on which exist the monadic, archetypal consciousness or the Kemetic Khu or Spirit. See James, 1988; King, 1990, 1992; Pryce, 1965; Powell, 1987; and Valerian, 1992; Browder, 1991

Attractive-to cause to approach, adhere, bond, charm.

Atum-A God of ancient Kemit. See, Budge 1991,1969

Autosomal Recessive-A genetic code located on one of the 22 pair of non sex deterrning but autosomal chromosome strands of D.N.A. in such a fashion or molecular structure that the same gene must be present on both of the same chromosomes Coming from each parent for the gene to be expressed and made into a actual body structure. If Another gene code structure for a dominant code is present or the same code is not present of the other chromosome of the pair the gene will not be expressed.

Axon- The arm of a brain cell, neuron, upon which an electrical charge, flow of electrons serves as a pathway leading into the body of the cell and then passes out through many dendritic arms at the opposite end of the neuron that then passes the electrical current into the axon arm of an adjacent neuron.

Bantu-A name used for African people in the southern regions of the African continent.

Beatific Vision-Another name for Inner Vision. A state of beatitude or upmost bliss. See James,1988; Valerian, 1992; Powell,1987; King, 1990, 1992, 1994.

B.C.-Before Christ, a dating system that dates in a yearly fashion dates that decrease in number on approaching the supposed birthday of "Jesus the Christ". The year before that birthday being year 1 and actually corresponds to year 29 after the Roman conquest of Greek-Ptolemy occupied Kemit. Two years before the Christ birthday being B.C. 2, three years before the Christ birthday being B.C. 3. Note there is no historical evidence of the existence of the personality of "Jesus the Christ" but there are direct parallels of the alledged life of "Jesus" to the earlier Kemetic diety Hero and over 30 other 'Messiahs' in different cultures around the world. See Ben-Jochannan,1970,1981 ; Kuhn, 1944, 1949; and Jackson, 1985.

B.C.E.- Before the Common (Christian) Era, a yearly dating system that counts each year before the present time without consideration for the Christian based A.D. dating system. Thus 2 B. C.E. is 2 + 1994 A.D. or 2 + 1994 = 1996 B.C.E

Beast-An animal or human without inner vision, with feelings and goals that center around satisfying animal drives, love is experienced primarily as Genital sexual feeding. See Powell, 1987; King, 1990, 1992; and Valerian,1992.

Benzothiazine-a chemical compound that exists as a six sided ring structure with a Carbon atom at each comer.

Binocular Vision- The coordination of the vision of the two lateral eyes such that a single image is seen.

Black Cubit-A Kemetic system of measurement, the Nilometric cubit used by Kamites whenever they worked on a Black Stone. See

King. 1990.

Black Dot- The Point, Yod, Dalath, Door, Spermatozoa, A Symbol for the Creative God Energy emanating or projecting into the various levels of manisfestation of Nun, Space, Primeveal Waters of Nun. The Nun/Melanin Door through which the energies of Life pass. See King, 1990,1991,1992, 1993.

Black Melanin- Eumelanin, Black to Brown Melanin. Black Melanin exists as Cosmic Melanin, Planetary Melanin, Plant Kingdom Melanin, and Animal Kingdom Melanin. See King, 1990,1991,1992,1993, 1994; Andrews, 1989; Barnes, 1988, 1993, Welsing, 1970, 1990; Hemmitt, 1992, 1993; Barr, 1983; Eberle, 1988; Ani, 1994; and Amen, 1993.

Black Stone of Pesslnus, Carthage-A black stone that was maintained, worshiped in Carthage and was taken to Rome following the last Punic War. See King, 1990.

Black Symbolism-A form of symbolism that upon meditation or intense concentration could evoke a projection of latent unconscious genetic memories onto the Black image being visualized. The psychospiritual process of Khem or alchemy. See King, 1990, 1992, 1993; jung, 1964, 1967,1974; Welsing, 1990, and Hemmitt, 1992, 1993.

Black Vision-A form of vision that is mediated by the rod rhodopsin based retinal mediated vision. This visual pigment which is mediated through the Melanin containing retinal pigment epithelium is processed in the occipital cortex as black and white contrast vision. See Creel 1980; Drager, 1986; Hood, 1976; Libennan, 1991; Path, 1978; Stevens, 1974.

Blastula- A stage in the embryological development of the pre fetus, a ball of cells that develops from the rapidly dividing cells resulting from the spermatozoa fertilized ovum. See King, 1990.

Blood Bourne Motile Melanin Computer- Melanin within White Blood Cells that as a Cell serves as a massive Melanin mediated Organic Cellular Motile Computer in the Vascular Tree and Local Ionic Environmental States critical for adherance and release of Hormone Signals bound to Protein in Blood. Critical to Melanin modulation of Ionic homeostatsis is the mediation of Calcium balance, the feedback loop to the H.B.B of the efficiency of H.B.B. translation of Light. See Wasserman, 1970, King; 1990,1994; Barnes, 1988,1993; Amen, 1993; Slominski, 1993; Strzelecka, 1982; Liberman, 1991; Lacy, 1981,1984, McGinness 1976, 1985; Holick, 1981, Jacobson 1992; Bulkey, 1989, Devreotes, 1994; Cope, 1981; Clemens,1982; Cohn, 1977; and Williams, 1990.

Blue (Water) Lilly-Nymphaea caerlea, the Black Nymph (minor Greek divinity, Elemental Entity, Deva Entity, a life form .undergoing Epigenetic Metamorphosis toward an Adult Imago form), the Black Nile Water Lily, taken by Kamites to induce trance states in which the free Soul or Ka could consciously visualize the entities on the other realms of consciousness such as the Nymphs vastly higher Angelic Life forms (Dieties) and the and the Anceslors (Immortals). See Emboden, 1989; Powell, 1987; Valerian, 1992, Bukley, 1989; King, 1990, 1991, 1992, 1993,1994; Welsing, 1990; Barnes, 1988,1993, Andrews, 1989; James, 1988; and Saraydarian, 1980.

Bone Density- The Measure of the amount of Calcium contained in Bones which in humans has been found to, be 10% greater in Black than White humans as a result of the influence of Skin color relationship to higher levels of pineal secretion of Melatonin in Blacks, higher parathyroid hormone blood level and higher vitamin D levels. See King, 1994; Clemens, 1982; Kiss, 1969 ;Csaba, 1968; and Holick, 1981;

Book of the Coming Fourth By Day (Book of the Dead)- The Holy Bible of ancient Kemit when there was an advanced Spiritual Education (later presented in a very different form as religion) in the form of the Pyramid Texts which later became the Coffin Text which even later became the Book of the Coming Forth By Light (Book of the Dead) which later appears as portions of the Holy Books of Islam and Christianity. See Faulkner, 1969,1978; Budge, 1967; and Karenga, 1990.

Brain Stem- The base of the Brain including the midbrain, pons, and medulla oblongota, contains the reticular acivating system and the limbic system. See Valerian, 1992; Powell, 1987; Andrews,1989

Brain Stem Reticular Formation-A nerve network in the brainstem that mediates an awake state of consciousness. See Valerian, 1992, Powell, 1987; Andrews, 1989

Brain, Twelve Pigmented Nucleui- A Melanin Tract of Neurons in the Brain Stem of Vertebrate Animals including all Humans. See King, 1990; Bazelon, 1967; Fenichel, 1968; Forrest, 1972, 1975, Graham, 1979, Lindquist, 1987; Lacy, 1981, 1984; Marsden, 1969; McGinness, 1976, 1985; Andrews, 1989

1. Locus Coeruleus- Black Dot, the principal norepinephrine nerve supply to the cortex. Involved in R.E.M. Sleep, Conscious recall of dream, Astral Events. The uppermost in a chain of Brain Stem Neuromelanin Nerve Tract, THE AMENTA NEUROMEIAN-IN TRACT, the only animal to have this Nucleus to be heavily pigmented. See Mann,1979; King, 1990; Sandyk, 1991; Powell, 1987; Valerian, 1992; Crosby,1962; Forrest, 1972,1975

2. Substantia Nigra- Black Substance,the 11th in a chain of Brain Stem Neuromelanin Nerve Tract, THE AMENTA NEUROMEIANIN TRACT, Loss of neuromelanin in this nucleus is known to result in the disorder known as Parkinson's disease. The treatment of Parkinson's disease is to give medications that are pre-cursors of Melanin to re- pigment the substantia Nigra Neurons. See Mann, 1979; King, 1990; Sandyk, 1991; PlJWell, 1987, Valerian, 1992; Barbeau, 1985, 1986, Barnes, 1988; Crosby, 1962; Forrest 1972, 1975.

3. Brachialis-See Forrest, 1972,1975; Cosby, 1962

4. Paranigralis-See Forrest 1972, 1975; Cosby, 1962

5. Intracapularis Subcerleus-See Forrest 1972, 1975; Cosby, 1962

6. Nervi Trigeini-See Forrest, 1972,1975, Cosby, 1962

7. Mesencephasius-See Forrest 1972,1975; Cosby, 1962

8. Pontis Centralis Oratis-See Forrest 1972, 1975; Cosby 1962

9. Tegmenti Pedennculopontis-See Forrest, 1972, 1975; Cosby 1962

10. Parabrachialis-See Forrest, 1972, 1975; Cosby 1962

11. Medialis Dorsomotor-See Forrest 1972,1975; Cosby 1962

12. Retro Ambigualis-See Forrest 1972, 1975; Cosby 1962

Broadcast- To project, emanate, transmit, scatter, sow seeds.

Buddhic Plane-A level of consciousness above the physical, and astral hut below the atmic. The level upon which the Soul is based and ftllly operative. See King, 1990, 1991, 1992; Welsing,1990; Powell, 1987; Valerian, 1992; Ani, 1994; Faulkner 1969, 1978;Budge, 1967; Piankoff, 1954,1977; and Karenga, 1992

Bull of Offerings-A Symbolic reference to Wosir (Osiris) in the Coffin Texts. See Faulkner, 1978, King, 1990,1991,1992

Calcium-A bivalent metallic element, atomic number 20, as an ion it serves as a feed back loop input to the W .B.B.M.S. in modulating the efficiency of Melanin mediated translation of light by various interelated cutaneous (skin) and non-cutaneous pools of Melanin. See King, 1994.

C- A.M.P .-cyclic Adenosine Mono Phosphate, A key chemical compound involved in intercellular energy production by translation of energy into and released by phosphate bounds in the C-AMP compound. See Barr, 1983 Devreotes, 1994

Carbohydrate-Chemical compounds that are one of the three forms of chemical energy for the body, the two others being protein and fats. Carbohydartes are different forms or sugar and are metabolized by the energy for rapid energy production in 30 minutes to one hour.

Carbon Dioxide-A chemical compound of one atom of carbon and two atoms of oxygen. This chemical compound is produced by animals as a product of animal cellular energy production and is then released into the atmosphere. This chemical compound is breathed into plants and is utilized by plants in energy production with oxygen released by plants as a product into the atmosphere. Carbon dioxide upon reaching high levels in the planet's atmosphere does serve to trap heat from escaping into space from the planet's surface and serves a critical role in the "greenhouse effect". Carbon dioxide upon reaching high levels in the atmosphere does promote the increase in *size* of plant growth. See Czerkas, 1991; Sichel, 1988.

Catalytic-an compound or agent that is unchanged itself but does increase the rate of a chemical reaction. Examples of a catalysis are the enzymes such as Tyrosinase and Tyrosine Hydroxylase, and in some respects Melanin. See Bukley, 1989; Devreotes, 1994; and Cope, 1981.

Catecholamfne-A class of chemical compounds that are amines, containing NH3 (nitrogen atoms bound to hydrogen atoms), such as epinephrine. norepinephrine, dopamine which are all precursors of Melanin. These chemical compounds serve as hormones and neurotransmitters in nerve tracts in the brain such as the tract located in locus coeruleus and in pheripheral autonomic nervous system, the sympatheric nerves that are involved high in attention states for willful motor activity. See Mann, 1979; MoIler, 1992.

Cation Exchange-A Chemical/ Physical reaction in which an Atom with a net excess of electrons will donate the excess electrons to a neighboring compound.

Caucasian- Commonly refered to as the White Man, a person for whom their ancestors since before 6,000 BC.E. were descended from an originally Black African people who either and or were superficially altered in high mountain regions Ice Age climatic conditions to have low skin melanin levels and Ice age specific modifications in their H.B.B., were genetic mutations, or selected breeding with forced exile for a 2,000 year period to the Caucaus Mountain regions of Eurasia. Current definitons of Caucasians include the social political concepts of Ani's definition of White Consciousness in the book Yurugu, Welsing's White Supremacy as defined in the book The Cress Theory of Color Confrontation and Racism (White Supremacy), Diop's definition of the Two Cradle Theory, Bradley's definition of White Supremacy White Consciousness relaed to present Neanderthal Glacial ecosystem Shaped behavioral patterns,and King definition of White Consciousness resulting from a Pineal Calcification and resultant lower Pineal Melatonin sel-'fetion mediated fixation in the Melanin medaited H.B.B. metamorphosis with predominance of materialism and ignorance if not distorted fear of spirituality. It is critical to consider Massey's reterence to ancient Kemetic references to Caucasians as the Tamahu, or Created Man. Other critical considerations of baseline different modifications of the H.B.B. that mediate cultural ecosystem intluced styles of consciousness such as White Consciousnes or Black Consciousness may been seen as different forms of consciousness expression during the course of the metamorphlJSis of the Melanin mediated H.B.B., the Salvation Ascension, or Freedom of the Soul Consciousness. Relative to the present day African Black consciousness the expression of some phases of White Consciousness in the form of Racism and White Supremacy is without question A Major Demonic Evil and Force that hampers the Fullness of Black Consciousness if not Life itself. Some landmark physical traits of Caucasians consist of a tendency for Pineal Gland Calcification, Skin Pheomelanin (Blond to Red Color), Skin types of Melanin production being of type I through IV with round skin Melanosomes and a skin Melanosome ability to produce Melanin ranging from no ability to tan (always develops skin sun burn inflamation upon exposure to sun light) to no sun burn with dark skin tan. Of the upmost importance is the fact that with changes in the planet's atmosphere UVC forms of light now reach the planet's surface and upon exposure to UVC Caucasian skin Pheomelanin is converted into Sulfur containing compounds that are carcinogenic and mutagenic, the rate of skin cancer of various forms is now doubling in Caucasian populations every ten year. Pheomelanin contains 9-12% sulfur whereas Eumelanin contains less than 1 %. See Meleski, 1977; Attias, 1985; Barr, 1983; Barnes, 1988,1993; Barrenas, 1990; Clemens, 1993; Cohn, 1977; Creel, 1980; Drager, 1986; Holick, 1981; Ito, 1993; lung, 1963, 1967,1974; King, 1990, 1994; Massey, 1973; Ani, 1994; Rosen, 1962; Royster, 1980; Slominski, 1993; Wassermann, 1970; Wel- sing,1970, 1990; Williams, 1990; Hemmitt, 1992,1993; ben- Jochannan, 1981; Bradley, 1992; Muhammad,1965; Guthrie, 1992

Cerebellum- A part of the brain above the medulla that *is* involved in equilibrium and coordination of muscle movement.

Chaos-a state that appears to the physical level of sensory organ perception to be in confusion and without order, a level of organization of form that may. be "Veiled or Black' to a strictly physical level of perception for those who are in darkness or ignorant of higher levels of sensory experience or knowing than just the physical level. See Bailey, 1925; Ashanti, 1990; King, 1990; Budge, 1971; Bulkey, 1989; Bynum, 1984, 1993, 1994; Chissell, 1993; Emboden, 1989; Ghalioungui, 1973; Hall,1972; Hillard, 1987; James, 1988; King, 1976; Massey, 1973; Stevens, 1974; Ukodari, 1978; Welsing, 1990; Waite; Valerian, 1992

Cholorophyll-A green plant photoreceptor critical for photosynthesis (plant Light transduction into chemical reactions for energy production and utilization by the plant. Chlorophyll absorbs Light up to wavelength 700 mu and is present in three forms (a,b,c). Chlorophyll is structurally similar to the red blood cell pigment hemin. Cholorophyll is the "Melanin" equivalent photo pigment found in the Plant Kingdom. See Hawley, 1977.

Children of Seth- A term used to, define the progeny of Seth, a symbol for Evil, or the Enemy of the Sun God Ra. See Faulkner, 1968, 1978; Budge, 1967, 1969, 1991; Karenga, 1990, 1991, 1992, 1993; Hemmitt, 1992, 1993

Chromophores-A chemical that produces color in molecules, the color corresponding to those wavelengths of Light that are not absorbed by the molecule but reflected away.

Cingulate Gyrus-An area of the brain that borders the corpus callosum, an area of the brain that unites the left and right cortical hemispheres. Surgically induced lesions of this area have been reo ported to result in visceral responses with a reduction of agitation, "paranoid anxiety". See Cosby, 1962

Clairaudence- The ascended sensory or Freedom ability that occurs with Melanin mediated metamorphosis to hear things that can not be heard with the physical ears without regard to time or physical location. Inner Vision, Seership.See Bailey, 1925; Emboden, 1989; James, 1988; King, 1990; Ukodari, 1978; Valerian, 1992;Welsing, 1990;

Clairvoyance- The ascended sensory or Freedom ability that occurs with Melanin mediated metamorphosis to see things that cannot be seen with the physical eyes without regard to time or physical location. Inner Vision, Seership. See Bailey, 1925; Emboden,1989; King, 1990; Ukodari, 1978; ValIerian, 1992;
Welsing, 1990

Coffin Texts-Ancient Kemetic Maps of the Spirit, Soul, and Mind. An earlier version of the later New Kingdom Kemetic Text of The Coming Forth By Day (Book of the Dead) that was developed from the Old Kingdom Pyramid Texts and appeared in the Middle Kingdom (2,100- 1,675 B.C.) See Faulkner, 1978, King, 1990, 1992

Coil-A shape in the form of a spiral or helix. See Bukley, 1989; Devreotes, 1994, VaJerian, 1992; King, 1990

Colitis-A disorder with inflammation of the inner lining of the Colon. See Liberaman, 1991

Collective Unconscious- The vast portion of the Unconscious which is by far the greatest part, the symbolic "Prirneveal Ocean " of the Kemetic Memphite Cosmology, the Kemetic "Nun", all Universes, all time/space/ creation, the Fabric of God, encompassing all levels of consciousness/unconsciousness including atmic and buddhic. See Assagioli,1965; Bailey, 1925; Hall, 1972; lung, 1988; King, 1990; Ukodari, 1978; Valerian, 1992

Color Vision-A form of physical vision in which the visible colors of Light are seen by the process of Light activation of photopigments in the cone receptors located on the surface of the retina that lines the inner surface of the eye.

Comprehension- The process of development of understanding, consciousness, meaning. See Ani,1994; Bailey, 1925; .King 1990; Ukodari,1978; Valerian, 1992

Conductor-A substance that is capable of transmiting energy such as sound, flow of electrons (electricity) Cones Color Vision sensory receptors on the surface of the retinal inner lining of the eye that when exposed to Light generate an electrical charge by cone photopigment absorption of Light which in turn passes the absorbed energetic light form as a chemical event into Melanin in the pigmented layer of the retina which then translates it into an electrical charge into the optic nerve tracts to the occipital cortex where the life form experiences visual images in color Consciousness- The state of being Aware, Comprehension, Meaning, that vary in levels in terms of the range of awareness that a life form visualizes for their precise and mutually transformative relationships between their Self or Soul and various dimensions of the outer world. See Ani,1994; Asante, 1990; Ashanti, 1993; Assagioli, 1965; Bailey, 1925; James, 1988; King, 1990; Massey, 1973; Ukodari,1978; Valerian, 1992

Conversation with the Immortals (Ancestors)-A level of consciousness present in humans who attain the Kemetic third grade, Sons of Light/Unity (Christ level) with Light in the Kemetic Mystery System. See James, 1988

Core-a portion of the Melanin molecule that absorbs U.V Light See Strzelecka, 1982

Cosmic Melanin-Melanin present as complex organic molecules in interstellar gas clouds. See. King, 1990; Valerian, 1992;Hemmitt, 1992, 1993; See Saraydarian, 1980

Cranial Sutures-A line of union between cranial bones.

Creative Genius- The expression of the soul after freedom from the fetters of the physical body, expression of the higher Angelic Self (Christ, Son of Light, Genius, Osiris, Perfect Black) after Melanin mediated metamorphosis of the H.B.B.-sensory organs. See Assagioli, 1965; Bailey, 1925; King, 1990; Ukodari, 1978; Valerian, 1992

Creators-Kemetic Son of Light stage. See James, 1988.

Crescent-The convex or concave shape of the moon at a stage between full moon and new moon. See Be:n-Jochannan, 1970;Massey, 1973; Jackson,1985;

Crystal-The, Kemetic name for crystal is thehent the same name for amber which in Greek is Elektron. See'Budge, 199.1

C.S.F.-Cerebral Spinal Fluid. A clear colorless fluid produced inside the ventricular chambers within the brain which circulates through the brain ventricular system and also over the surface of the brain and spinal cord, a critical freeway for the travel of H.B.B. hormones such as Pineal Melatonin to site in the interior and surface of the brain and spinal column. See King, 1990, 1994; Kitay, 1954; Valerian, 1992

Current- A flow of energy along a path such as with electrons along a toroidial or cylindrical path. See Bulkey, 1989

2-S-Cysteinyldopa-A mutagenic and carcinogenic form of Pheomelanin that is produced upon exposure to U.V. Light. See Koch, 1986

5-S-Cystelnyldopa-A mutagenic and carcinogenic form of Pheomelanin that is produced upon exposure to U.V. Light. See Koch, 1986

Cystitis-Inflammation or infection of the bladder See Liberman,1991

Cytotoxicity- A condition that is toxic or harmful to cells. See McGinness. 1976

Darkness-A state of not transmitting, receiving, reflecting, or radiating light. Ignorance. An illusionary state of fear often confused with Black which is an entirely different state in which Light transmission, reception, relection, and radiation is hidden from perception by underdeveloped sensory organs. See Ani,1994; Bailey, 1925; King, 1976; King, 1990,1994; Welsing,1970, 1990; and Valerian, 1992.

Decode- The conversion of various forms of Information, Light, Energy, into a form that has meaning.

Deification- The process of projecting onto an object the Unconscious images of Divinity, Alchemy. See Assagioi, 1965; Bailey. 1925; Budge. 1971; lung, 1963, 1969, 1974, 1979; King, 1990; Valerian, 1992.

Dimension-A number of sensory elements which determine. position of consciousness in space, time, and density of consciousness. See Valerian, 1992.

Dendritic Processing- The flow of electrons from the dendrite, a series of arms at the Posterior end of a nerve cell, to an adjacent axon of another nerve cell.

Desensitization- To make emotionally less responsive, to decrease the amount and intensity of emotionally tagged sensory image projections from various levels of the unconscious onto symbolically equivalent events in the external world. See Ashanti, 1993; Assagioli, 1965; King, 1990; Welsing, 1970; Valerian, 1992; Liberamn, 1991

Desire- To Will, Wish, Request, Order, Think or Visualize. See Assagioli, 1965

Diethylamine Melanin- A form of Melanin. See Thatachi, 1993

Dipole Monomer-A chemical/physical state present in electromagnetic systems that has two poles (positive, negative) that can undergo polymerization or bonding of similar compounds in a chain by each positive pole being bound to the negative pt)le of the adjacent monomer unit. See Bulkey, 1989

Discrete-A distinct unconnected element Djed Column- A Divine Object In the Kemetic Mystery System with the life process being the development of the student with the ability to raise the Djed Column from a horozontal (dead, undeveloped state of consciousness) to an Upright, Perpendicular to the Planet Earth (Full Consciousness, Freedom of the Soul).See Amen, 1993; King, 1990,1992; Budge, 1968,1991.

D.N.A.-Deoxyribonucleic acid, located in the cell nucleus, this is the chemical map containing the chemical genes of heredity as a double helical coil. See Bulkey, 1989; Jacobson, 1992

Door-A symbol for Melanin as Black Dot, Yod, Spermatoza, and Dalaath. In Kemetic literature the hieroglyph for door during most of the dynastic period contained the pictrograph of testicles and an erect penis. A means of Archway or Archetypal access to energy translation into other forms and dimensions. See King, 1990; Waite; Ponce, 1973; Spencer, 1984; Saraydarian, 198Q; (Piankoff (Book of the Gates),1954

Dopamine-A chemical neurotransmitter present in nerve tracts in the brain, a chemical that is blocked by the action of antipsychotic medication in the supression of psychosis, the overwhelming of the ego by poorly integrated elements from the lower unconscious. A precursor of Melanin. See King, 1992; Barnes, 1988; Bailey, 1925; Assagioli, 1965; lung, 1969

Dragon-Serpent. See Piankoff, 1954, 1977; King, 1990; Forrest, 1972, 1975; lung, 1963,1969,1974; Budge, 1912,1967,1969, 1991; Ben-lochannan, 1981; Czerkas, 1991

Dreams-A state of consciousness of various levels of awareness of being in different dimensions which includes R.E.M. sleep (conscious recall of dreams by neophytes) and Non R.E.M. sleep (no conscious recall of dreams by neophytes but conscious recall by Melanin transformed humans with Soul Freedom Inner Vision comparable to Grade 2. Intelligence. or Grade 3, Son of Light, of the Kemetic Mystery System). Full sensory Ascension is experienced in many forms of Dream or Individual or Group Trace States such as Projection with or without materialization/dematerialization See Assagioli, 1965; Bailey, 1925; King. 1990, 1992; Ukodari, 1968; Powell, 1987; and Valerian. 1992; Bynum, 1984,1993,1994

Dynamic Turnover-Electron or Energy Flow as it moves through the doughnut shaped torous magnetic field into the center, Black Dot, with movement through the cylindrical solenoidal magnetic field and opening, white dot, onto another torous shaped field at the opposite end of the cylinder with harmonic resonsance interplay of all elements present within the entire system, See Bulkey, 1989

Ectodenn- The outermost of three germ layers of an embryo, contains Melanin. See Pearse, 1969,1976; Barr, 1983; King, 1990

Eczema-A imfammatory condition of the skin.

Educational Academy-A School of Instruction of the Knowledge and Development of the Will to experience Self Development, inner Vision Meaning of Life. See James, 1988, Ben-Jochannan, 1981

Egyptian Mystery System- The name of the Kemetic Eduational Academy. See James, 1988, Ben-Jochannan, 1981

Electromagnetic- The system produced by a flow of electrons with a magnetic field perpendicular to the line of movement of the electrons. See Bulkey. 1989; Bailey. 1925, Powell, 1987; Hall, 1972; Valerian, 1992; Amen, 1993

Elecktron- The Greek name for amber .

Electron-Photon Coupler- The process by which a flow of electrons is absorbed into a chemical compound such as melanin and is converted into vibratory movements (sound) of polymer arms connected to the melanin compound. See Lacy 1981, 1984

Electron Transfer- The transfer or translation of electrons/energy from one atom to another. See Lacy, 1981,1984

El Ka'aba- The Shrine of Veneration of the Black Stone, Black Meterorite originally brought to Mecca from Ethiopia in the Religion of Islam in Mecca, Arabia. See Ben-Jochannan, 1970; Nicholson,1975

Empyrean-Celestial, Sublime. See Pryce, 1965

Energy-the capacity for doing work, natural power, Light, the Flow of Electrons. See Bulkey, 1989; Valerian, 1992

Enveloper- To cover, A Kemetic concept. See Piankoff 1954, 1977; Budge, 1991

Epidemiology- The branch of medicine concerned with the populational mathematical statistics that define the incidence, distribution, and control of disease in a population. See King, 1976; King, 1990; Welsing, 1970, 1990; Ani, 1994; and Valerian, 1994

Epidermal-Melanin Unit-In skin a system of organization. Each Melanocyte controls 36-40 skin cells. See Slominski, 1993

Epidermal Tripod-In skin a system of organization. Each Melanocyte and one Langerhans cell controls 36-40 skin cells. See Slominski, 1993

Epidermis- The surface layer of skin. See Slominski, 1993

Epiphysis Cerebri- The Pineal Gland. See Kitay, 1954; Reiter, 1982; King,1990, 1992

Epopteia (Beholding, Facing, Iniation)-A Psychological and Spiritual Rebirth, Melanin mediated Metamorphosis,Transformation, Ascension of Sensory Organs, Soul Freedom, Attainment of Inner Vision, See Pryce, 1965

E.S.P.-Ascension of the Sensory Organs. See Bailey, 1925; Ukodari, 1978; Valerian, 1922

Etheric Being-Consciousness on the Astral Realm. See Powell, 1987; Bailey, 1925; Valerian, 1992

Ethiopia-An ancient North East African nation, parent nation of Kemet and child of Khui Land. See. Ben-Jochannan, 1981: King, 1990, 1992, 1993

Extrapyramidial Disorder-A group of disorders with various distortions of movement, emotions and thought content that result from defects in nerves tracts in the brain stem. Parkinson's disease is one example of such disorders. See Cosby 1962; Forrest, 1972, 1975

Eumelanin-A Black to Brown form of Melanin. See Meleski, 1977; Barnes, 1988, 1993; Montagna, 1993; Slominski, 1993; Strzelecka, 1982; Sichel, 1988; Ortonne, 1993; Ito, 1993; Erickson, 1993

Eye of Horns- The Kemetic Eye of Inner Vision, Pineal Gland. Seership. See King, 1990, 1991, 1992, 1993, 1994; Kitay, 1954; Reiter,1982

Eternal Internal Sun- The Spirit/Soul or Kemetic Khu/Ka. James, 1988; King, 1990

Extrasensory -Ascension of the sensory organs. See Ukodari, 1988; King, 1990, 1992; Bailey, 1924; Assagioli, 1925; Valerian, 1992

Fasting-A consciously induced state of avoidance of external food that allows the body to shift from sugar, carbohydrate, metabolism into fat metabolism, which is energy efficient and also a means of clearing the body of toxins that were stored in fat cells, a state that occurs naturally during the usual neophyte sleep period of 6-8 hours with associated profound utilization of the endocrine mediated H.B.B. correlates of sleep and dreaming. Ancient Kamites stressed that good health care was partially based upon a good diet and did include periodic fasting. See Muhammad, 1965; Chissel, 1993; Devreotes, 1994; James, 1988

Female-Symbolically and naturally one of the two major aspects of Energy in the Universe, the other being Male. See Ben-Jochannan, 1970, 1981; King, 1990, 1992; Ani, 1994; Welsing, 1970, 1990; Pryce, 1965; Powell, 1987; Bailey; 1925; Ukodari, 1978

Fetters-Chains, as in the example of the emotional chains that bind the soul to the physical body-fear, gluttony, etc. See James, 1988

Fetus-An unborn vertebrate life form that has developed the basic structure of its kind. See Pearse, 1969, 1976; King, 1990; Erickson, 1993

Filaments-A single thread. See Bulkey, 1989

Flesh or Re-Skin Melanin, The Sun God Ra during the Nighttime. See Piankoff, 1954,1977; King, 1990

Flux-A Flow of a stream of Energy, Light, Electrons. See Bulkey, 1989; Devreotes, 1994

Forty Two (42) Books of Tehuti (Hennes)- The Books of Supreme

Knowledge used in the education of the various orders of Humans in the Mystery System Education of Kemit. See James, 1988; King, 1990

Forty Two (42) Declarations of Innocence (42 Negative confessions)- The Declarations of Supreme Knowledge used in the education of the emotional (Heart) and development of the Will of Humans in the Mystery System of Kemit See Ben-Jochamlan, 1970; Budge, 1961; King, 1990, 1992 (Kemetic Images of Light)

Free Radical Chemicals- A chemical molecule or compound that is not electrically neutral in charge, is lacking in electrons in its outermost orbital shell such that it will take such electrons from neighboring molecules thereby creating a chain reaction of altered molecules that are unstable and thereby disrupting those cellular processes that involved such molecules. See Barnes, 1988; King, 1990.

Fruiting Body-A body that bears the seeds of the genetic plans for self-replication of the same organizational type. See Bulkey, 1989; Deverotes, 1994

Genetic Loci- The actual site of the chemical structure of genetic code located on a strand of D.N.A.. See Jacobson, 1992

Global Thinking-A state of consciousness that is neither left cortical (analytical logical) or right cortical (emotional, analogical) but the result of the union of the two cortical hemispheres, Inner Vision, Freedom of the Soul, Melanin mediated metamorphosis of the H.B.B. See Ani, 1994; King, 1990, 1992; Valerian, 1992; Bynum, 1993,1994

GnRh-A hormone released by the hypothalmus that acts upon the anterior lobe of the pituitary gland to release the hormones that control the developmental cycle of the ovaries (estrogen) or testicles (testosterone). See Sizonenko, 1986

Gonadarche- The sex steroids, estrogen, secreted by the female ovary and testosterone, secreted by the male testes. See Sizonenko, 1986

Gonadotropins- The hormones released into the blood from the anterior lobe of the pituitary gland that affects the ovary and testes, F.S.H. (Follicle Stimulating Hormone) and L.H. (Lutenizing Hormone). FSH and LSH determine the menstrual cycle by controlling the maturation of the ovum (egg, germ cell) inside the ovary and the release of estrogen by the ovum. A comparable cycle is mediated by FSH and LH in the testes by control of the maturation of the spermatozoa (Black Dot, Yod, germ cell) by influence of the Sertoli cells in the testes and resultant release of Testosterone. See Sizoenko, 1986; King, 1990

Gout- A disorder in which the enzyme required for the metabolism of the Purine is not present and as a result the ingestion of protein food, animal meat, will result in the accumulation of Purine based crystals that accumulate in limb joints, kidney, and ear lobes with considerable pain and disability. In Kemit this disorder was referred to as the "Finger of Tehuti" (Helmes). See Liberman, 1991; King, 1990

Great One- A term in the Coffin Text referring to the Supreme Being or Highest God of the Universe. See Piankoff 1954, 1977

Habenula- A portion of the Brain that is the stalk and base to which the Pineal Gland is attached at one end and the posterior floor of the Third ventricle at the other end. See Sandyk, 1991; Reiter, 1992

Hannibal-A Supreme example of African Male leadership of the Warrior Class. This Great African General over the course of more than ten years repeatedly defeated entire Roman armies more than twice the since of his own army and occupied all of Italy except for the city of Rome during the second Punic war between the North African nation of Carthage and Rome. A Major Mrican Centric Study of the three Punic wars, Climatic conditions then present in North Africa, the personality of Hannibal Barca, strengths and weaknesses of the leadership class of Mricans in Carthage and Europeans in Rome and their impact on the reemergence of White Supremacy (Imperial Rome) and White Supremacist Multinational Corporate entities is required of present and future generations. See Polybius (Scott-Kilvert, Translator, Radice, Ed.), 1979, ben-Jochannan, 1981

Harmonic-A frequency of vibration or Light energy wavelength that is a integral (whole number) multiple of the fundamental frequency, same note with different pitch higher or lower than another note {fundamental frequency) 'See Valerian, 1992; Bulkey, 1989; King, 1990; Bailey, 1925 .

H.C.G.-Human Chorionic Growth Hormone-A chemical compound produced by the early fetus rooted in the wall of the womb, uterus, that promotes the growth and develop of the fetus and inner lining of the uterus to support the nourishment of the fetus. Pregnancy tests determine pregnancy by testing for the presence of this hormone. The other major hormone produced by the early fetus at the same time as HCG is M.S.H., melanoctyte stimulating hormone, a hormone that directs the growth and development of Melanocytes. See King, 1990; 1992, Slominski, 1993; Breathnatch, 1988; Drager, 1986; Eberle, 1988; Erickson, 1993

Helical-A spiral shape, the shape of the coil of D.N.A., the shape of the coil of African hair, the last setting of a star before it first rises after being invisible from a conjunction with sun, relating to the sun. See Valerian, 1992; Ortonne, 1993

Herpes-A viral infection of skin that produces inflammation. See Liberman, 1992

Heteropolymer Melanin- The Melanin Molecule being a complex Compound containing many different sub units such as metals, proteins. amines. fats, carbohydrates, etc. See. Barr, 1983; Slominski, 1993; Strzelecka, 1982; Menon, 1983

Hermes- The Greek name for the Kemetic diety and Ideal Human Type by the display of Intuitive Analytical Powers of the Soul, The Ideal Genuis, The Geni hidden within the human body, The Ideal Soul which is set Free by an actual metamorphosis of the H.D.B. Known by the symbolic name Mercury during the time of the Roman

Empire. Known by the name Genius in the current world. See Boylan, 1989; Bayley, 1968; Budge, 1969; King, 1990., Dames, 1988; 1993; Welsing, 1970, 1990

Heru-Kemetic name for the Child produced by the Union of Opposites, Male (Wosir, Wr, Osiris) and Female (Isis, Ast) See Karenaga, 1990; King, 1990, Budge 1969

Hidden Chamber- The Third Ventricle, The Location of the Soul in the physical body, The Cave of Brahman. See King, 1990, 1994; Kitay, 1954; Baker,1977; Bailey, 1925; Reiter, 1982; Ashanti, 1990; Hall, 1972

Higher Mind- The Soul. See King, 1990; Assagioli, 1965; Bailey, 1925; Ukodari, 1978; Valerian, 1992

Hillock-A raised potion of the neuron membrane surface where the axon arm joins the body of the neuron cell. A place where neurome-lanin in pigmented neurons is present to assist by "electron tunneling" the flow of electrons into the cell body. See Lacy 1981,

1984

Hippocampus- A raised portion of the floor of the lower area of the horn of the lateral ventricle in the Brain. See King, 1990; Barr , 1983; Bynum, 1993,1994; Valerian, 1992

Holy- Whole, Perfection, Transcendance, Ascencion, Saved Soul, Free Soul. Attainment of Inner Vision. See Ben-Jochannan,1970; Bailey, 1925; Ani, 1994; Bynum , 1993, 1994; Kuhn, 1944, 1949; Valerian, 1992

Horus- The Greek name for Hero. See Heru.

Horus of the Horizon (Re)-A Kemetic name for the Symbolic Concept of the Rising Sun (Soul). See Budge, 1969; King, 1990, 1992 (Kemetic Images of Light); Piankoff, 1954, 1977

Hypopigmentation-A "Relativistic" state of low pigmetation when considered in the context of an environmental matrix other than the one in which a life form developed a pigmentation pattern different than a parent form that allowed the form to exist and flourish in a new climatic ecosystem. See Slominski, 1993; Erickson, 1993; King, 1990, 1992, 1994; Barnes, 1988, 1993; Welsing, 1970, 1990; Ashanti, 1990; Ben-Jochannan, 1981; Clark, 1992; Cohn, 1977; Guthrie, 1992; Ani, 1994; Hall, 1972; Bailey, 1925; Powell, 1987

Hypothalamus-A portion of the Brain on the front posterior floor of the third ventricle that secretes various releasing factor hormones into a blood vessel portal system that directly controls the release of hormones by the pituitary gland which is directly below the hypothalmus. The hypothalamus is controlled by hormones released by the pineal gland such as melatonin. See Sizoneko, 1986; King, 1992; Valerian, 1992; Reiter, 1982; Kitay,
1954

I-33 Tissue of Horus-A Kemetic term present in the upper register Right Panel of the Second Shrine of Pharoah Tutankhamun that refers to the Melanin mediated H.B.B., the Spinal Column Axis (Djed Column) Series of glandular relationships to the Skin and Non-Skin Pools of Melanin. See King, 1990, 1992 (Kemetic Images of Light) 1994; Slominski,19,93; Breathnatch, 1989; Barr, 1983; Pearse, 1969,1976; Piankoff, 1954,1976

I am- The identification with a particular state of consciousness See Pryse,1965

Idealism- The philosophy that there are levels of reality above the physical realm. See Pryce, 1965; King, 1990, 1992; Assagioli, 1925; Bailey, 1925; Ukodari, 1978; Powell, 1987; Valerian, 1992

Imagination- Visualization of forms of organization of energy in a state of consciousness. See Pryce, 1965; King, 1990, 1992; Assagioli, 1925; Bailey, 1925; Ukodari, 1978: Powell, 1987; Valerian, 1992; Ben-Jochannan, 1983

Inflammatory Response-A biological state of "Celluar mediated Stress, Repair, Regeneration, Transformation, and Metamorphosis of the H.B.B.. See Slominiski, 1993; Montagna, 1993

Inner Ear- A portion of the ear in which the movement of bones in the middle ear is translated as mechanical fluid waves of the endolymph fluid of the inner ear to move the stereo Celia Hair cells that thereby generates a flow of electrons carried by nerves underneath the celia as the movements passes from the celia through the Melanin containing Stria Vascularis to the nerve tract into the brain auditory nerve tracts for processing and emanation of "Meaning". See Attias, 1993; Barr, 1993; Barnes, 1988, 1993; Barrenas, 1990; Bulkey, 1989; Cope, 1981; Forrest, 1972, 1975; Hood, 1976; King. 1990; 1992: 1994; Kono, 1980; Liberman, 1991; Lacy. 1981, 1984; McGinness, 1973, 1976; Meyer zum Gottesberge. 1988

Inner Vision- Defined in Kemetic Universities IIS II State of Profound Consciousness that become operative upon Freedom of the Soul from the chains of the physical body following a precise education and development of the will of the Human, II Melanin meditated metamorphosis of the H.B.B. See James, 1988; Piankoff, 1977; King, 1990, 1992, 1994; Valerian, 1992; Powell, 1987; Bailey, 1925; Ukodari, 1978

Intellect- The process of visualization of various levels of Consciousness with increasing levels of precision in the ability for greater resonance with environmental forms of energy in the fulfillment of one's life Mission, Golden Thread. See Pryce, 1965, Bailey, 1925, King, 1990, 1992; Valerian, 1992

Interstellar Gas Clouds- Vast clouds of Gas found around the centers of Galaxies in which new stars are formed. These clouds are known to contain complex organic molecule, Melanin. See King, 1990,1992, Valerian, 1992

Insulin-A hormone released by the Islet of Langerhans cells of the Pancreas that serves as a carrier compound in transporting sugar,

Glucose, into the interior of cells for the production of energy. The Langerhans cells are a part of the Melanocyte cells series and Epidennal Triad and are related to the A.PU.D. Melanin mediated endocrine gland system of the H.B.B. See Slominski, 1993; Pearse 1969,1976; King, 1990

Intuitive-A state of ascended sensory organ perception of consciousness. See Bailey, 1925; King, 1990; Powell, 1987; Assagioli, 1965; Ukodari, 1978; Valerian, 1992

Ion Permeability- The ability of Ions (molecules that are not electrically neutral but with positive or negative charge) to cross cell membranes. See Lacy 1981, 1984; Barnes, 1988; Bulkey, 1989, Devreotes, 1994

Islam-A Religious system whose major prophet was Mohamet of Arabia, 6th century A.D., and whose Holy Bible is the Qu'ran. See Ben-Jochannan, 1970; Nicholson, 1975

Israel-According to the Christian Bible (Gen. 32, 22-31) The name given for a state of consciousness that developed in a place named Penel (Pineal Gland [Eye of Hero] mediated Inner Vision), Is Ra The God, Facing God Ra, a name of a geographic region formerly known as Cannan, the place where the Hebrew following an Exodus from Egypt did develop the political state Israel. See Ben-Jochannan, 1970, 1983~ King, 1990,1992 (Kemeic Images of Light)

Intelligences- The second Grade of the Three Grade System of Levels of Consciousness attained by students in the Mystery System of the Kemetic University. Students of this level did experience Inner Vision, and Nous (Freedom of the Soul) See James,1988

Invagination- The formation of the Gastrula stage of the early vertebrate fetus by an infolding of the outer Melanin containing Ectoderm wall of the Blastula. See King, 1990; Pearse 1969, 1973

Iris- The color containing central outer portion of the Eye Ball. The amount of pigment of the Iris has been correlated with the amount of

Neuromelanin Brain pigment and Extracutaneous pools of Melanin in such sites as the Inner Ear. See Hood, 1976; Meyer zum Gottesberge. 1988

Jacob-According to the Bible (Gen. 32: 22-31), a name for a State of Consciousness, Yacub according to Hon. Elijah Muhammad, Guthrie, Hemmitt. The Mummy according to Gerald Massey, a Patriarch of the Jewish Religion., See Christian Bible, Gen. 32: 22-31; Guthrie, 1992; Muhammad, 1965; Hemmitt, 1992, 1993, Massey, 1973 (Yo. 1); Powell, 1987 (definition of Human Artificial), Ben-Jochannan, 1983

Jesus-A state of consciousness of the Christ Level, Sons of Light, Unity with Light Grade of Student in the Kemetic University.There is no historical record of the personality Jesus the Christ in recorded history but there are many references to Ideal Human Types of Christ-Like personalities throughout the world in various cultures and thousands of years before the Christian Era in Kemit there was the diety Hem. See Kuhn, 1944,1949; Massey 1973; Jackson, 1985; Clark 1992; King, 1990, 1992; Piankoff, 1954, 1977; Faulkner, 1969, 1978; Budge, 1967, 1961,1969; Karenga, 1990; Kerenyi, 1959

Jet Black-A Black Colored Ore with "Magical Properties "that resulted in the Kemet Khem (Chemistry, IKhemy) process of separating Gold and Silver from the Earth (Raw Earthem Ore) by the Use of Mecury. See Alchemy

Ka aba-A Shrine of a Black Stone, Black Metorite, originally brought to the Shrine in Mecca by Ethiopians before the time of the Prophet Mohamet. See Ben-Jochannan, 1970; Nocholson, Nicholson, R.A., 1975

Kamites-A name for the Black African Human inhabitants and Rulers of ancient Kemit, Egypt. See Ben-Jochannan, 1981; Karenga, 1990

Kamt-Ancient Kemit; See Ben-Jochannan, 1981

Karma-A positive or Negative Force produced by a person's ethical History of Conduct. See Budge, 1961,1969; King, 1992 (Kemetic Images of Light); Powell, 1987

Kemet-Ancient Egypt. See Ben-Jochannan, 1981

Kerationcyte-A skin cell, part of the Epidermal Triad, Epidermal Melanocyte Unit, See Slominiski, 1993

Key-Something that provides a solution to a riddle, a small switch for opening and closing an electrical circuit, a device that will turn the bolt of a lock on a Door. Melanin is a Key that turns the Bolt, Series of Genes that Had blocked Expression of another section of DNA which when operative induced a profound Metamorphosis (Transformation) of the Human form with Ascension and enhanced integration of Sensory Organs resulting in a State of Consciousness at Unity with Light, Able to experience higher Octaves of Harmonic Resonance with High Physical and Transphysical Entities of Light/ Energy. See Bulkey,1989; Devreotes, 1994; Bailey, 1925; Pryse. 1965; King. 1990, 1992, 1994; Ukodari, 1978; Valerian, 1992

Kheme- The Kemetic Black product of the "Alchemical Process" See Alchemy. See Budge, 1971

Khemeia- Kemit, Egypt. See Alchemy. See Budge, 1971

Khepri- The Rising Sun, God Ra in Ascension, The Human Soul in Ascension. See Budge, 1969; King, 1992 {Kemetic Images of Light)

Khui Land-A Supreme Name of a Supreme Place, The Land of The Birthplace of the Gods, The Original Holy Land, THE LAND OF THE DOUBLE SHADES, The land Represented in the Book of the Coming Forth by Day as the Land between the Lakes or Ru and Kharu, The land of the Birth place of the Anu; The land around the Lake of Mwanza (Lake Victoria), The Great Lakes Regions of North East Africa [Goma] 1; The land at the Foothills of the Mountain of the Moon {Papyrus of Hunnefer}, The Mother and Father of Ethiopia., THE LAND OF THE BIRTHPLACE OF HUMANITY.

See Ben-Jochannan, 1981; Brunson, 1992; King, 1990, 1992 (Kemetic Images of Light); Churchward, 1978; Budge, 1969

King's Chamber, Great Pyramid of Ghiza- The Uppermost Room in the Great Pyramid at Ghiza and said to be a Vault of Initiation of the Mystery System for the University System of Per Ankh, House of Life in Kemit. A room that is an All Black Room, with all Walls, Floor, Ceiling and Open Sarcophagus being Black Rose Granite. (A Black Cube) See King, 1990, 1992 (Kemetic Images of Light)

Kupffer Cells-Reticuloendothelial Cells (White Blood Cells) that line the sinusoids of the Cells of the liver and contain Melanin and other pigment compounds. See Sichel, 1988

Lady of Letters- The Goddess Setkhet. See Budge, 1969; King, 1992 (Kemetic Images of Light)

Lamellar-A thin plate

Langerhans Cell- A star shaped cell in the skin and a spindle shaped cell in the Pancreas. See Slominski, 1993; Montagna, 1993; Pears, 1969,1976; King, 1990

Lattice-A Door having a lattice such as geometric arrangement of fissional be material in a nuclear reactor, a neural network (Epidermal Triad, Epidermal-Melanocyte Unit), a regular geometrical arrangements of cells or Melanin Molecule sub units over an area of space. See Cope, 1981; Bulkey, 1989; Devrotes, 1994

Left Cortex- The analytical Cortex. See King, 1990

Library and Museum of Alexandria-A Library and Museum established on the Kemetic Mediterranean Sea Coastline at a place later Named the City of Alexandria by the European/Greek warrior Alexander under the guidance of his childhood tuitor Aristotle. This Library was formed from books stolen from the Kemetic University, The Mystery System of Kemit, whose central administration was in Luxor, with multiple world-wide Branches, a with a most illuturous history of over 4,000 years of continuos history and achievement by African Female and Male Professors before the invasion of Kemit by Greece, following a 2,000 year history of major climatic/geological decay [Sahara Desert] in North Africa. See James, 1988 King, 1985, 1990, 1992, 1994

Life-Light, Energy. See Bulkey, 1989.

Light-Energy, See Bulkey, 1989; King, 1990, 1992;Valerian 1992

Limbic Cortex (Limbic Forebrain)-An anatomically connected system in the brain composed of the hippocampus, hypothalamus, and amygdala that are involved in the experience of emotions and motivation. See Forrest 1972, 1975; King, 1990; Valerian, 1992

Literalist-Word for Word, Utilizing a standard frame of reference of consciousness. See pryse, 1965

Lupus-A disorder that is an autoimmune disorder in which the body's own immune system mediated by white blood cells attack and destroy its own cells and organs as "alien" of the same body, with particular focus upon the skin, skeletal joints, and heart. See Liberman, 1991

Lymph-A lluid vascular tree that drains into the veins and carries lymphocytes, a cellular type that mediates the body's immune system and cellular responses to inflammation. Lymphocytes carry Melanin, Circulating Melanin, in those Humans with Dark Skin pigmentation Types 4-6. See Slominski, 1993; Wassermann, 1970

Lymph Nodes-A mesh of connective tissue located at frequent inter-vals along the yphatic fluid filled vasculature that serves as a filter. Over 50% of Bantu's were found to have Melanin in their lymph node, circulating Melanin. See Slominski, 1993; Wasserman,1970

Lymphocytes-A cell type known to be critically involved in A.I.D.S., See Lymph, Valerian, 1992

Macromolecular-A large Molecule. See Bulkey, 1989

Magic-Heka-The use of the Will. See Assagioli,1965; Ashanti, 1993; Piankoff, 1954, 1977; King, 1992 (Kemetic Images of Light); Bailey, 1925; Powell, 1987; Massey, 1973; Budge,1971

Male-One of the Two major Aspects of Light/Energy in the universe, the other being Female. See Ben-Jochannan,.1970, 1981; King, 1990, 1992; Ani, 1994; Welsing, 1970, 1990; Pryse,1965; Powell, 1987; Bailey, 1925, Ukodari, 1978

Mandragora Officinarum-Mandrake, Used in the Kemetic induction of Trance states. See Emboden, 1989

Mecca- The Holy City and Holy place of the Religion of Islam, site of Holy Shrine of the Ka' aha. See Ben-Jochannan, 1970

Median Forebrain Bundle-A system of ascending and descending Brain nerve fibers connecting the olfactory centers of the medial hemisphere wail with the preoptic and hypothalmic areas and possibly the midbrain. See Cosby, 1962

Medina-A city in Arabia and site of residence of the Prophet Mohamet of the Religion of Islam. See Ben-Jochannan, 1970

Melanin- The Chemical of Life which has a unique structure that allows it to absorb Light/Energy over a vast portion of the range of wavelengths of the radiant Light Energy spectrum and to transform energy into various other forms of energy to allow the melanin containing life form to self -replicate and to progressively experience harmonic resonance (meaning, self-replication enhancement) with higher forms of Light radiation. This molecule serves as a transformation Door lm the levels of the Cosmic, Planetary, Plant Kingdom, and Animal Kingdom. See Amen, 1993; Ani, 1994; Ashanti, 1993; Barr, 1983; Barnes, 1970, 1993; Ben- Jochannan, 1981; Bradley, 1992; Breathnatch, 1988; Bynum, 1994; Cesarini, 1988; Clemens, 1982; Cohn, 1977; Cope, 1981; Creel, 1980; Crippa, 1978; Drager, 1986; Eberle, 1988; Fenichel, 1968;Forrest, 1972, 1975; Graham,

1979; Holick, 1981; Hood, 1976; Jung, 1963, 1974, 1979; King, 1990; 1992, 1993; Kono, 1980;Lacy, 1981,1984; McGinness, 1976,1985, Meleski, 1977; Mishima, 1992; Nordlund, 1989; Ortonne, 1993; Pears, 1969, 1976; Montagana, 1993; Prose, 1965; Santamarina, 1958; Sichel, 1988; Slaminski, 1993; Strzelecks, 1982; Tata, 1969; Thatachari, 1973; Wassermann, 1970; Welsing, 1970, 1990; Willaims, 1990

Melanocyte- The cell type that produce the Hormone Melanin in skin and non skin sites such as the inner ear. See King, 1990, 1994; Barr, 1983; Slominski,1993; Ortonne,1978; Meleski,1977

Melanophorus- The Order of the Kemetic Mystery System University that specialized in the study of Black Symbolism and Melanin. See Brunson,1991; James, 1988

Melanosome-An organelle or specialized compartment of the Melanocyte inside of which Melanin is made and stored. See King,1990, 1994; Barr, 1983; Slominski, 1993; Ortonne, 1978; Meleski, 1977

Melatonin-A hormone released by the Pineal Gland during Night. See King, 1990, 1991, 1992, 1993, 1994; Kitay, 1954; Reiter,1982

Menopause-A phase of Life during which a female ceases the monthly Menses and no longer produces ovum, which accompanies major H.B.B Endocrine realignments. See Sizoneko, 1986

Menses-A roughly 29 day cycle during which a fertile female ovulates with responding fluctuations of Pituitary F.S.H. and L.H. and Ovary Estrogen. Major mental/Soul access variations occur during different portions of the menstrual cycle particularly the week preceding the onset of menses, blood flow following the breakdown of the uterine wall when no implantation of a fertilized ovum has occurred following mid cycle ovulation. See Sizoneko; Liberman, 1991

Mental Plane- A plane of consciousness of largely analytical organization of experience but without intuitional focused perceptions or utilization of ascended sensory organ observations or reflections. See Assagioli, 1965; Bailey, 1925; King, 1990, 1992; Powell, 1987; Valerian, 1992

Mental Slavery-A condition of Enforced Stagnation or Fixed Development in which the oppressed human remains alienated from his or her soul by the use of propaganda manipulation of consciousness and enforced miseducation. The Focus is one of Fear over the loss of material security and avoidance of pain while examples of high achievement, and inspiration for self replication, self education, self meaning, and high levels of self replication are commonly ignored or falsely labeled as crazy. See Ashanti, 1990; King, 1990; Barnes, 1993; Welsing, 1990, James, 1988

Mercury- The Planet closet to the sun in our solar system, The Roman name for Tehuti. See Massey 1973; Saraydarian, 1980

Metiss-A human of mixed ancestry, semi Black, White or Asian.

Micro Black Hole-A quatum event, a space/time entity the size of a component of the atom such as an electron.

Middle Eastern Population-A human whose ancestors have resided in the Middle East, between Africa and Asia, commonly called Semetic. During the time of the New Kingdom Kamites such persons were called Asiatic. However in even earlier Old Kingdom times such persons were call Dravidian and even earlier the Anu. Throughout all of these times major portions of humans living in these regions have been and continue to be Black Africans. See Ben-Jochannan 1981,1983

Milky Way Galaxy- The Galaxy in which our Planet, Sun, and Planetary family exist. It takes roughly 250,000 years for our planetary family to make one orbit around the center of the Milky Way Galaxy. Our planetary family is about 2/3 of the way out along the radius from the center of the galaxy and is about half way from the horizontal axis of the Galaxy as it move upwards towards the vertical axis. Valerian, 1992

Mind-A state of consciousness that is largely analytical or lower emotions. A state of consciousness that is by Kemetic definitions still Neophyte, either right or left brain focus but without a union or synthesis of the two cortical hemispheres. See King, 1990, 1992; Ani, 1994; James, 1988

Mistress of the House of Books- Sefkhet. See Budge, 1969; King, 1992; James, 1988

Mononuclear Cells- White Blood Cells, a part of the Immune System. See Wassermann, 1990

Morphogenesis- The change in shape of a life form throughout the genesis or developmental history of the life form. See Dverotes, 1994

Morula-An early stage of the vertebrate prefetus following fertilization of the ovum by the spermatozoa in the female fallopian tubes, the black berry. See Erickson, 1993

Motilities-Form Structures that emanate through the Flow of Electrons of a Life Form that is Self Replicating. See Bulkey, 1989

Mortals-Neophytes as a grade defined for students in the Kemetic University Mystery System. See James, 1988

M.P.P.-A chemical compound that selectively bonds to pigmented, neuromelanin containing brain neurons. See Barbeau, 1985

M.P.T.P.-A chemical compound that selectively bonds to pigmented, neuromelanin containing brain neurons. See Barbeau, 1985

M.S.H.-Melanocyte Stimulating Hormone, a hormone produced by the pituitary gland that induces the melanocyte to increase melanin production. See Eberle, 1988

Music- The Science and Art of ordering tones in succession to produce a composition that has Harmonic Resonance. See James, 1988

Musical Choir- The composition of a Musical experience composed of many different elements all exprssed as Unified Whole (Holy) in Harmonic Resonance. See Bulkey, 1989

Mutagenesis- The production of mutations. In the case of pheome-lanin, mutageneis occurs when UV light is absorbed by Pheomelanin it produces three different forms of sulfur containing pheomelanin metabolites that bind to skin cell DNA and cause misreading of DNA, i.e. mutations. See Koch, 1986

Mutation-See Mutagenesis

Netherworld-A Kemetic term for the Underworld or states or Levels of the Unconscious. See Piankoff 1954, 1977; Budge, 1961, 1967, 1969, 1971; Bailey, 1925; Assagioli, 1965; Powell, 1987; King, 1985, 1990, 1991, 1992, 1993, 1994; Ani, 1994; Ukodari, 1978

Neural Crest-A area bordering around the neural tube that forms as an investigation of the Blastula ectoderm, prefetus, from which orig-nate the cells that later become Melanocytes, Pinealocytes and many other endocrine glands that comprise the A.P.U.D. cell series portion of the H.B.B. See Barr, 1983; King, 1990; Pearse, 1969, 1976; Slomiski, 1993; Erickson, 1993

Neural Network-An analog computer comparable to the structure of the Epidermal Triad. comprised of an input layer. one or more pro-cessing layers. and an output layer in which by repeated data pro-cessing runs all elements of the computer serve as a whole memory lattice and progressively arrive at closer approximations of a "best fit" answer to the question asked of possible associations between data points. See Slominski. 1993; Valerian. 1992

Neural Tube-A tube formed in the vertebrate gastrula pre fetus that later become the brain and spinal column. The neural tube is formed as an evagination of the blastula Melanin containing ectoderm. See Erickson, 1993; Pears, 1969, 1976; Slominski, 1993

Neuromelanln-Melanin present in Brain neurons. See Brain Pigmented Nucleui

Nueromelanin Granules-Melanin in the cytoplasm or cell body of Neurons. See Brain Pigmented Nucleui Neuron- Brain Cells that are involved with the processing of the flow of Electron currents. See Bulkey, 1989; Devoretes, 1994; Valerian, 1992; King, 1990, 1994

Neurupeptides-Protein hormones, particularly those that mediate emotions such as possibly the endorphins. See Slominski, 1993; Eberle, 1988, Sandyk, 1991

Neuropeptlde Y -A neuropeptide present in the sympathetic nerve supply to the Pineal Gland. See Moiler, 1992

Neurotransmitters-Chemical compounds that mediate the flow of electrons between nerves, across the synaptic space between adjacent nerves. Many of these neurotransmitters are precursors of Melanin. See Barr 1983; King, 1990, 1992, 1994; Bulkey, 1989; Devoretes, 1994

Neutron Star-A star whose nucleus is composed entirely of neutrons, this occurs after an earlier star developmental history in which the star explosion and implosion whose force was so great that the protons in atoms at the core of the star were converted into neutrons by the fusion with electrons

Night Blindness-An inability to see at night, related to retinal defects in rod photoreceptors or other elements in the retina or visual nerve tracts. See Drager, 1986

Nilometric Cubit- The Black Cubit, a Kemetic Linear measurement used only by Kamites when working in Black Stone. See King, 1990

Noetic-Related to the Intellect. See Pryse, 1965; Bailey, 1925; Powell, 1987: Valerian, 1992; King, 1990, 1992

Non-Resistive-A system in which either is a highly efficient and ease of now of electrons such as in a semi-conductor, super conductor, electron-phonon coupling. See Cope, 1981; Lacy,1981, 1984; Valerian, 1992

Noradrenergic-A neurotransmitter in sympathetic nerves, precursor of melanin. See Moiler, 1992; Barr, 1983; King, 1990

Norepinephrine- a neurotransmitter in sympathetic nerves, precursor of melanin. See Moiler, 1992; Barf, 1983; King, 1990

Nun- The Primeveal Waters, Cosmic Blackness and possibly Cosmic Melanin. See James, 1988 (Memphite Cosmology)

Nutritional Practices-See Fasting

Nymphaera Caerula-See Blue Water Lilly

Oasis of Yathrib-An Oasis in Medina were the Prophet Mohamet of Islam lived in exile for six years. See Ben-Jochannan, 1970

Oculocutaneous Albinism-A form of albinism that involves a lack of melanin in the visual tracts with some forms also associated with enlarged skin melanocytes See Creel, 1980; Drager, 1986

Ocular-Cutaneous Melanin-Melanin present in the skin and retinal pigmented epithelum. See Creel, 1980; Drager, 1986

Odorants-Chemical compound that activate major neurotransmitter pathways of the Melanin mediated W .B.B.M.S. See Devoertes, 1994

On-A Kemetic City site of a major College of the Kemetic University Mystery System. See Budge, 1991; Ben-Jochannan, 1981

One Hundred Eighty Degrees (180)- The Opposite of an element.

Optic Cup- The embryological structure from which develops the vertebrate Eye.

Optic Nerve- The second cranial nerve which runs from the Eye into the visual nerve tracts into the brain occipital cortex. See Drager,1986

Optic Nerve Tracts-Optic nerve tracts that are present in the visual cortex of the occipital lobe. See Drager, 1986

Optokinetic Nystagmus-A constant fluttering of the eye in either a horizontal or vertical direction. See Drager, 1986

Orynx-A gazelle. See Faulkner, 1978

Oscillator-A structure that moves back and forth, See Bulkey,1989

Osteoporosis-A disorder of low bone density, low calcium content with frequent bone fractures and bone curvatures. See Bone Density

Osiris- The Perfect Black God of the Underworld or Unconscious. See Budge,1961, 1969; King, 1985; 1990

Ovoid Melanosome-An oval shaped Melanin containing melanosome that is usually found in Blacks or Asian Humans. See Meleski, 1977

Oxidant Atmosphere-An atmosphere high in Oxygen in which Melanin serves a critical role to neutralize oxygen free radicals. See Sichei, 1988

Ozone-A compound of Oxygen with three atoms of Oxygen, which in the upper atmosphere serves to absorb U.V.C. Light.

Paraquat-A compound which heavily binds to Melanin. See Barbeau, 1985

Parathyroid-A gland present in the neck that releases the hormone parathyroid hormone, which pulls calcium out of bone storage sites.

The release of this hormone is controlled by the Pineal Gland. See King, 1994; Pearse,1969, 1976

Parasympathetic Nerves- The part of the Peripheral Nervous System, Autonomic Nervous System, with the major neurotransmitter being Acetylcholine, involved in contemplative, meditative states of consciousness, part of the nerve supply to the Pineal Gland. See Moller,1992. See Acetylcholine

Parkinson's Disease-A disorder in which there is a selective loss of neuromelanin in the Substantia Nigra. Upon consideration of the lower incidence of Parkinson's disease in high skin Melanin African people as compared to low skin Melanin African people there is mounting evidence that there are relative correlations between the amount of cutaneous melanin and neuromelanin. See Substantia Nigra. See Hood, 1976.

Pastophorl- The ancient Kemetic order for all Female and Male Physicians, who had to know six additional Books of Tehuti. See James, 1988; Ghalioungui, 1973,1983

Patmos- The island of Phelan. See Muhammad, 1965; Guthrie, 1992

Peniel-Pineal Gland, Pine Cone, Eye of Hero. According to the Christian Bible, Gen. 32: 22-31, it was at this place that Jacob met the angel of God and was transformed into Israel. See Pryse, 1965; Baker, 1977; Kitay, 1954; Reiter, 1982

Penuel-Pineal Gland, Pine Cone, Eye of Hem. According to the Christian Bible, Gen. 32: 22-31, it was at this place that Jacob met the angel of God and was transformed into Israel and the Sun shone on the hollow of his thigh, (Femoral Triangle). See Pryse, 1965; Baker; Kitay, 1954; Reiter, 1982

Peptide Histidine Isoleucine-A neuropeptide and vasoactive peptide present in the parasympathetic nerve supply to the Pineal Gland. See MoIler, 1992.

Per Ankh- The House of Life, The Kemetic University Healing Center (Hospital). See James, 1988; Ghalioungui, 1973, 1983

Perlkaya- The body of the nerve cell containing the nucleus and cytoplasm.

Peripheral Nerves-AII nerves outside of the Brain and Spinal column, autonomic nerves with sympathetic/ parasympathetic divisions, sensory nerves, voluntary motor nerves See Cosby, 1962

Personal Unconscious- That portion of the unconscious that contains memories of what a human has experienced in their life time, from gestation/birth to the present. See Assagioli, 1965; King, 1990

Pheomelanin-Skin Melanin of 6-11% sulfur content, blond to red in color, present more frequently in skin types I-IV. See Ito, 1993; Meleski, 1977; Ortonne, 1993

Photon-A particle of Light. See Valerian, 1992

Photon-Electron Coupling- See Electron-Photon Coupling.

Photophobia-A fear of Light, often present in humans with Oculocutaneous Albinism. See Drager, 1986

Photoprotection- The role of skin melanin absorption on U.V. light in protection of skin cell DNA from genetic code alternations, mutagenesis and or carcinogenesis. See Meleski, 1977; Cesarini, 1988; Ortonne, 1993

Phrenic-Diaphragm, relationship between the volume of inspiration/expiration rate of respiration, O_2 and CO_2 concentrations mediated by melanin energy metabolism, CSF acid/base conditions induced by changes in breathing patterns (Hatha Yoga) and resultant changes in states of consciousness. Relating to the mind in which disorder of states of consciousness (Schizo PHRENIA) occur in response to intrusions into consciousness of lower unconscious entities. Considering Pryse's cryptic 1910 A.D. notation of the Seer or

Patamos and the Dragon of Darkness, The Beast or Phrenic Intellect. See Pryse, 1965; Assagioli,1965; King, 1990,1994; Ani, 1994; Hemmitt, 1992,1993

Phylogenesis- The development of a word, custom, genetically group of life forms as compared to an individual

Pineal Gland- The Eye of Hero, The Soul Eye, Eye of Inner Vision, The Pineal Gland, The Penis, Glandula pinealis, The Epiphysis Cerebri, The Pine Cone, The Master Gland, The Father, Black Dot, The Thousand Petaled Lotus, A Rose in Bloom, The Crown, The Crown Shakra The Fourth Eye, The Eyes in the Back of the Head. A Supreme major endocrine portion of the H.B.B. that translates Light into endocrine hormone messengers for a vast myraid of effects and mediates the use of human. Will in the visualization of dream image plans to organize the modeling of the external world into the ideal dream image, a channel of communication and travel to the various other levels of consciousness including conversation with the ancestors. See Ani, 1994; Assagioli, 1965; Bailey, 1925; Baker, 1977;Barr, 1983; Barnes,1988, 1993; Bayley, 1968; Ba7..elon, 1967; ben-Jochannan, 1981; Boylan, 1979; Byan, 1974; Bulkey, 1989;Budge, 1961, 1967,1969. 1971; Bynum, 1993, 1994; Chissell, 1993; Cope, 1981; Eberle, 1988; Emboden. 1989; Faulkner; 1969,1978; Fenichel, 1968; Forrest, 1972, 1975; Frenkel; Hall, 1972; Hemmitt, 1992, 1993; Hillard, 1987; Hood, 1976; Jackson,1985; Jacobson, 1992;; James, 1988; June, 1963, 1974, 1979; Karenga, 1990; Karenyi, 1959; King, 1976; King, 1978-1994, Kitay, 1954; Liberman, 1991; Lacy, 1981,1984; McGinness, 1976, 1985;Moller, 1992; Muhammad, 1965; Nobles, 1985; Pearse, 1969, 1976; Pelham, 1973; Piankoff, 1954, 1977; Ponce. 1973; Powell, 1987; Montagna, 1993; Quay, 1974; Reiter, 1982; Sandyk, 1991; Santamarina, 1958; Saraydarian, 1980; Sizoneko, 1986; Slominiski, 1993; Stevens, 1974; Strzelecka, 1982; Tota, 1969; Ukodari, 1978; Valerian, 1992; Vaughn, 1986; Welsing, 1970,1990; Williams, 1990; Woodroffe, 1973; Young.

Pizeoelectric Effect- The emanation of a flow of electrons from a crystal when pressure is applied to a crystal.

Planar Group-A structure having a two dimensional quality.

Planetary Melanin-Melanmines, Melanin related substances that exists as naturally occurring chemical compounds in the upper layers of the planet's crust.

Plant Kingdom Melanin-See Chlorophyll

Polarizing- To influence Light to take form into various patterns, to display opposite patterns of form.

Pole Star- A Star that is directly over either the South Pole or North Pole. See King, 1990; Churchward, 1978

Porasis- An inflammatory skin disorder. See Meleski, 1977

Post Traumatic Stress Syndrome- A disorder in which upon exposure to symbolically meaningful reminders of past personal or genetic ancestor experienced traumatic events the human will experience stress laden memories of past (Emotionally Stressful, Karmic) and present traumatic events in the present in an emotionally magnified stressful ego fixating condition. See Assagioli, 1965; King, 1990; lung 1963,1974,1979

Pre-Adamadic Man-See Adam-Kadmon

President of the Library-See Sefkhet. See James, 1988, Chapter 7

Projection-See Alchemy

Propaganda-Consciousness control of public opinion by the distorted presentation of reality. See Ashanti, 1990; Ani, 1994

Prophet Mohamet-See Islam

Prostitute-See Phrenic

Protein Carrier Molecule-A protein that serves to carry ions across membranes or to transfer electronic charges from the charged ion into other systems of flows of electrons within the Melanin molecule. See King, 1994

Pseudo-False, Illusionary, See Phrenic.

Psoralen-A chemical precursor of Melanin. See Meleski, 1977

Psychometry- The ascended sensory organ experience of touch by which touching or being near an object will reveal to the sensitive person experiences concerning the owner of the object. See Bailey, 1925; King, 1990; Powell, 1987; Ukodari, 1978; Valerian, 1992

Pterygopalatine Ganglia-A ganglia connected to the parasympathetic nerve tract the serves the Pineal Gland. See Moller, 1992

Ptolemanic Period- The Period of Greek occupation of Kemit, 332 B.C. -30 B.C., See ben-Jochannan, 1981

P. T .S.-A measure of the ability and sensitivity to hear sound. See Barrenas, 1990

Pulsar-A Cosmic source of pulsating radio waves.

Pupil of the Eye of Hero- The Black Dot center of the eye through which light enters into the anterior Light translating retinal pigmented epithelial (RPE) surface. See Faulkner, 1978; King, 1990

Pyramdion-Capstone, often Black sometimes Gray in color, located on the top of the Pyramid. See Chissell, 1993; King, 1990

Pyramid (Great, Khufu) Pyramid of Ghiza-A site of Initiation in the Kemetic Univesity Mystery System of ancient Kemit.

Pyramid Texts-Old Kingdom Kemtic Texts of Iniation into the various levels of consciousness, Mind Maps of Consciousness. See Faulkner, 1969; King, 1990

Qemt-Kemit. See Budge, 1971

Quasars-Cosmic objects that emit vast emanations of Light

Qu 'ran- The Holy Bible of the Religion of Islam

Ra- The Kemetic Sun God. See Budge, 1969. See Light. See Bulkey, 1989; King, 1990; Valerian, 1992; ben-Jochannan, 1970, 1981

Radio-Waves-A portion of the electromagnetic spectrum of wavelengths of Light. See Valerian, 1992

Realm-Kingdom, Domain, Sphere of Influence of an energetic entity. See Pryse, 1965

Receptive-Able to absorb and translate energy, ideas.

Red Blood Cell-A cell in the blood that carries oxygen in a form bound to hemoglobin.

Red Giant Star-A star in end stage of development in which it assumes a large size and red color as its consumes through nuclear fusion the last sources of fuel in its core.

Reducer Atmosphere-to combine with or be subject to the actions of Hydrogen, to assume a lower oxidation state.

Regeneration-transformation, Self-Replication. See Bulkey,1989

R.E.M. Sleep-A phase of consciousness in which can recall dreams. A state of consciousness of 30-45 minutes duration that occurs 3-4 times each period of 6-8 hours of sleep. See Dreams.

Replications-Reproduction. See Bulkey, 1965

Repulsive- To Repell, Negative.

Resonance-enrichment of a musical tone by intensification through the additive effect of a tone in play of the same note but at a different octave or integral wave length of vibratory rate of the tune. See Stevens, 1974; King, 1990;'Bailey, 1925; Bulkey, 1989; Valerian,1992

Retina- The Inner lining of the Eye that contains the rod and contain the rods and cones Light sensory receptors for the translation of light into electron flows for nerve transmission into the Brain visual Cotex. There is a critical Pigmented layer of the retina that contributes the c-wave in the retinogram. See Drager, 1986; King, 1994

Retinal Pigmented Epithelium (R.P.E.)- See Retina

Retinohypthalamic Tract-A segment of the Sympathetic Nerve tract from the lateral eye to the Inner Eye, Pineal Gland. This nerve tract segment runs from the eye to the suprachiasmatic nuclei of the hypothalamus. See Murphy, 1986

Rhodopsin-A photopigment in rods that absorbs photons of light and later transfer the photon into Melanin in the Pigmented Layer of the Retina (RPE). See Drager, 1986

Right Cotex- The cortical Hemisphere that is largely involved in analogical emotional processing. See King, 1990; Valerian, 1992

Rods-Light sensory receptors located on the surface of the retina that are involved in the perception of Black and White Vision.

Rose Granite- See Black Granite.

Salvation- The Life Process of Freedom of the Soul through the Kemetic Process of Education of the Human and Development of the Will to become free of the chains of the body, to become of sole visualization of the contents of the lower unconscious. Melanin mediated metamorphosis of the H.B.B. with ascension of the Sensory Organs with enriched Self-Replication, Higher Octaves of Resonance with higher Levels of Light (Faster moving waves of Light) See James, 1988; King, 1990, 1994; Bailey, 1925; Powell, 1987; Ukodari, 1978; Valerian, 1992

Scarab-Khepra, The Kemetic Symbol of the rising Sun, The Ascension of the Soul upon Freedom of the Soul from the Chains of the Body, See Budge, 1969; King, 1992 (Kemetic Images of Light)

Scavenger- To remove an undesirable elements from an environment such as in the ability of Melanin to remove free radical oxygen ions. See Barnes, 1988; 1993; Barr, 1983,

Sciatica-A disorder of the sciatic nerve in the posterior leg with pain along the route of the distribution of this nerve.

Seer-A person with Clairvoyance, and other ascended sensory organ functions. See extrasensory perception.

Seffhet-A Kemetic Goddess who is a consort of Tehuti, She receives ideas directly from the Supreme God and instructs Tehuti as what to write in the Book of Life. See Budge, 1969; King,1992

Setket-See Seffuet

Sefkhet-See Seffhet

Self Meaning-Self-Replication, The Experience or visualization of forms of energy, ideas, relationships that result in ascension of the sensory organs, Melanin mediated transformation, harmonic resonance with one's spiritual order. See James, 1988; King, 1990; Powell, 1987; Ukodari, 1978; Bailey, 1925

Self Transformation-See Self-Meaning

Semiconductor-A substance that is able to carry energy as an efficient rapid flow of electrons with greatly reduced to such flow. See Cope, 1981; Lacy 1981,1984

Serapis-A Greek Ptolemy period in Kemetic history when Tehuti was expressed in the Kemetic symbolic image of Serapis and later the Messiah image of the Christ (Unity with Light) of Jesus in

Christianity or as an Aviatar or Messenger in Mohamet in Islam or Buddha in Buddahism. See James, 1988; King, 1990; Powell, 1987; Bailey, 1925; Boylan, 1979

Serotonin-A hormone released by the pineal gland into blood during day, or exposure to Light. See Kitay, 1954; King, 1990,1992; Reiter 1982

Sesheta-See Seffket

Seth- The Kemetic symbol of Evil. See Ben-Jochannan, 1970, 1981, 1983; Boylan, 1979; Bailey, 1925; Powell, 1987; King, 1990,1992; Valerian, 1992; Hemmitt, 1992, 1993;Budge, 1912, 1969, 1971; Faulkner, 1969, 1978; Karenga, 1990;
Sexual Attraction-Bonding between opposite sexual forms for mutual ascension and freedom of the soul. See Bulkey, 1989; Devoretes, 1994

Sex Hormones-Hormones produced by the female ovaries, estrogen, and male testicles, testosterone. See Pearse, 1969, 1976; King, 1990

Shaman-a Priest. See Ashanit, 1993; Emboden, 1989

Shamanistic Trance-A trance enduced in a human by a Shaman. See Emboden. Trance is also known as a form of Inner Vision. See Inner Vision. See Ashanti, 1993

Shu-The Kemetic God of the air. See Ben-Jochannan, 1981; Budge,1969

Shrine of Tutankhamun (Second Shrine, Right Panel, Upper Register)-A Critical Kemetic Shrine found over Pharaoh Tutankhamun's sarcophagus that contained Cosmological Concepts of Kemit See Piankoff, 1977; King, 1990

She Who Is Provided With 7 Horns- The Kemetic Goddess Sesheta. See Sesheta, Seffket.

Sleep-A State of Unconsciousness/ Consciousness. See REM sleep and Non REM sleep. Social Communication-Communication between individual life forms of a community that functions as an integral whole. See Deovretes, 1994.

S.O.D. Catalases-A catalysis that is mimed by Melanin. See Sichel, 1988

Solenoid-A coil that is often in the form of a cylinder and is used to carry a current or flow of electrons. See Bulkey, 1989; Amen, 1993

Sons of Light- The third and final stage of the Educational Process of ancient Kemit. Unity with Light See James, 1988

Soul-A state of consciousness that is operative in the Kemetic Educational Process of grade 3, Sons Light. A state of Ascension, in which the Melanin mediated H.B.B. undergoes a metamorphosis of the sensory organ receptors allowing a Freedom of the Soul. See James, 1988; King, 1990; Bailey, 1925; Powell, 1987; Valerian, 1992; Assagioli, 1965; Ani, 1994

Spore Cells-A reproductive cell that upon fusion with another spore will develop into another life form. See Devreotes, 1994

Spinal Cord-A major portion of the Central Nervous System (CNS) that carries nerves from the brain into the spinal column with segmental levels of nerves leaving the spinal column at each vertebrate along the spinal column. See Cosby, 1962

Spirituality-A State of Consciousness of profoundly expanded awareness that was achieved by a process of Educational initiation in the Kemetic University Mystery System Grade 3, Unity with Light. A Melanin Mediated Metamorphosis of the H.B.B.. Endocrine (APUD) System facilitated Sensory Organ Ascension. A State of Being in which a Human through the process of Heroic Struggle has Developed the Knowledge and the Will to Free their own Soul from the Chains of their own Latently Divine Physical Bodies (Temple) to Develop Inner Vision, An Operative Eye of Heru. See King, 1990;

Ukodari, 1988; Welsing, 1990; Barnes, 1993; Ani, 1994; Ben-Jochannan, 1970, 1981; Karenga, 1990; Clark, 1993; Ashanti, 1993

Spiritual Consciousness-See Spirituality

Spiritual Entities-Life Forms with a Spiritual Consciousness. See Spirituality. See Powell, 1987; Bailey, 1925; Budge, 1969; Valerian,1992

Stalk Cells-Cell found in the cyclindric shaped column or trunk of a life form, fruiting body. See Bulkey, 1989; Devreotes, 1994

Stratum Corneum- The outer layer of skin. See Meleski, 1977

Stratum Malpighi-Also known as the stratum germinativum, the germative layer. a inner layer of the outer epidermis layer of skin resting on the bottom layer of the stratum coreum, See Meleski, 1977

Super Conductor- A substance that has almost no resistance to a current or flow of electrons. Melanin has been reported to have semi-conductor and super conductor attributes. See Cope, 1981

Super Conscious- A Realm of the Highest Level of States of Spiritual Consciousness within the Collective Unconscious. See Assagioli. 1965; Jung, 1963, 1974, 1979; King, 1990, 1992; Jacobson; 1992

Superior Cervical Ganglia-A collection of cell bodies of the sympathetic nerves in the chain of sympathetic nerves that link the external Eye with the internal Eye, The Pineal Gland, The Eye of Heru. The last link in the sympathetic chain of nerves before such nerves reach the Pineal Gland. See Murphy,1986; Reiter, 1982

Suprachiasmatic Nucleus or the Hypothalamus-A collection of Brain nerve cell bodies through which passes the sympathetic nerves that link the eye with the Pineal Gland. This Profoundly important site is also now believed to be the physical correlate of the site of the Internal Clock that sets the circadian rhythm of glandular activity in the Whole Body. See Murphy, 1986; Reiter, 1982

Sufi-A Mystical Order within the Religion of Islam. See Nicholson, 1975

Testicle- The "Family Jewels", Male. Organs found within the Scrotum that produce the Male reproductive germ cell, The Spermatozoa, and male Hormone, Testosterone. See Pearse,1969, 1976; King, 1990, 1992 (Kemetic Image of Light)

Thalamus-A large oval mass of the cell bodies of Brain cells in each lateral wall of the Third Ventricle, these cells are profoundly involved in the translation of meaning given to sensory experiences. See Cosby, 1962; Valerian, 1992

Thehent- The Kemetic word for Amber and Crystal. See Budge 1991

Thermoregulatory- That which regulates heat or the temperature present in a system. Melanin serves a critical role as a thermoregulator in the Animal Kingdom. See Sichel, 1988; Czerkas, 1985; Finch,1991

The Book of What is in the Netherworld-A Kemetic map of the Unconscious Mind present in the tomb of Ramses VI. See Pillnkoff.1954

Third Eye- The Eye of Hem, The Eye of Inner Vision, The Pineal Gland. See Eye Of Hem, Inner Vision, Pineal Gland, Melatonin, Serotonin.

Third Ventricle-A Supremely Important Chamber within the midline of the Brain, said by the ancients to be the abode or seat of the Soul while in the physical body. The Pineal Gland is located in the floor at the posterior end of this chamber. The Hypothalmus and Pituitary Gland is located in the floor of the anterior end of this chamber. The pineal hormone Melatonin is present in this chamber in a level of concentration that is thirteen times greater than blood levels of melatonin. Critical consideration was given by the ancients to the relationship of the four bodies that surround the Habenular stalk to which the Pineal Gland is attached, The Back of the Human Body and the Back of the Adam Kadmon. Vast areas of potential research await further study of the CSF contacting Neurons, some of which are said by Vigh and VighTeichmann to line the walls of the Third Ventricle and are said to be migrating Pinealocytes, and the role of the CSF as a major route for transport of multiple hormones to receptor sites that line the inner walls of the Brain ventricular system and spinal column central canal. See Vigh,Vigh-Teichmann, 1992,1975,1977,1980; Baker; King, 1990,1994; Ponce, 1973; Kitay, 1954; Reiter, 1982; Valerian, 1992; Cosby, 1962

Three- The Symbolic number of Unity, the Child resulting from the union of the Female and Male, Third Grade of the Kemetic Mystery System. See James 1988, Piankoff, 1954,1977; Ponce 1973

Threshold Switch-A switch or lock that when a Key is applied will that act as a Door to open and close the flow of electrons. Melanin is a Key. See Key. See Bulkey, 1989; Devroetes, 1994

Thyroid-A Gland in the neck that is part of the A.P.U.D. Endocrine Glandular component of the H.B.B .See A.P.U.D., King, 1994.

Thyrocalcitonin Cells-Cells in the thyroid gland that produce the Hormone, Thyrocalcitonin, a Hormone that serves to inl,'fease Bone Density by increasing Calcium incorporation into Bone. See A.P.U.D., King, 1994

Toroidal-A Doughnut Shaped Form of the Flow of Electrons at Both Ends of a Cylinder, See Bulkey, 1989, Deovretes, 1994

Toxin-A Poison.

Trance States-A State of Unconsciousness/Consciousness, Transphysical travel and Inner Vision. See Emboden, 1989

Transformation Plane- The plane of Consciousness present after metamorphosis of the Melanin mediated Ascension of the sensory organs through a profound harmonic Resonance of the H.B.B., Freedom of the Soul. See Pineal Gland, Melanin, Inner Vision, A.P.U.D.

Transmembrane-Across the cellular membrane

Transmuted- Transformation. See Alchemy.

T .T .S.- Temporary Threshold Shift. A measure of the ability to hear sound. Melanin determines different levels of T .T .S. See Hood, 1976

Tyrosinase-An enzyme in skin melanocytes that produces Melanin from the amino acid Tyrosine. See Slominiski, 1993, Lindquist,1987

Tyrosinase Hydroxylase-An enzyme in the brain that produces Melanin from the amino acid Tyrosine. See Lacy, 1981

Twa-The Annu, See Churchward, 1978; Budge,1969; King, 1990, 1992 (Kemetic Images of Light), Brunson, 1992; Finch, 1991

Ultrasound Sound-wave energy of a particular speed of vibration, Melanin is critically involved in the translation of sound energy. See Meyer zum Gottesberge, 1988; Kono, 1980

Ultrastructure- The structure of matter when observed at magnifications of 200,000 times normal 20/20 vision when using an electron-microscope.

Uncovering (Unveiling)-See Iniation

Underworld-See the Netherworld

Unth- The name of a district or country referred to in the tomb of Ramses VI. See Piankoff, 1954

Uterus- Black Dot, The Holy Womb of Life, The Holy Vessel, The Holy Alchemical Bath. See King, 1990. See Alchemy.

U.V.A.-Absorbed by the core of Melanin. The slowest form of UV light. See Shosuke, 1993

U.V.B.-Absorbed by the core of Melanin. A faster form of UV light. See Shosuke, 1993

U.V.C.-Absorbed by the core of Melanin. The fasted form of UV light, usually absorbed by the upper atmosphere Ozone layer, but with Ozone depletion this form of UV light is now reaching the planet's surface and upon being absorbed by skin Pheomelanin will produce three forms of sulfur containing metabolites of Pheomelanin that are Mutagentic and Carcinogenic. See Shosuke, 1993; Strezelecka, 1982; Koch, 1986; Cesarini, 1988

Vasoactive Intestinal Peptide- Piptides present in the parasympathetic nerve supply to the Pineal Gland. See MoIler, 1992. See Parasympathetic

Vertebrate-A bone in the spinal column. See Cosby, 1962

Vibration-Speed of movement of Matter. See Bulkey, 1989, Stevens, 1974, Valerian, 1992. See Phonon-Electron Conversion, Light.

Vicious-A state of matter that continually alters shape when exposed to a force. See Cope, 1981

Visions-See Inner Vision

Visualization-See Inner Vision

Vitamin D-A critical vitamin that is a carrier compound for the transport of calcium in ingested food in intestinal tract across the intestinal membrane surface into blood vessels for whole body distribution. This hormone exists in an inactive form which is made active in skin

upon exposure, to light, a light activated vitamin. Skin Melanin serves a critical role in determining the amount of vitamin D activation in relationship to the changes in climate mediated levels of sunlight See King, 1990, 1994; Ani, 1994,
Williams, 1990

1. 7- dehydrocholestrol vitamin D-Pre Vitamin D

2. 25-hydroxy vitamin D- An intermediate form of Vitamin D made by light activation, passage of a photon of light into the vitamin D molecule

3. 1,25 (OH) 2 vitamin D- A final a fully active form of vitamin D made in the kidney tuble by the action of parathyroid hormone. See King, 1990, 1994; Ani, 1994; Williams, 1990

White Blood Cells-Blood Cells that comprise a major portions of the Immune System. Melanin circulates in the blood in white blood cells. See Wasermann, 1990;Slominski, 1993

White Eye or Heni- The Sun. See King, 1992 {Kemetic Images of Light); Budge, 1969

White Vision-A form of vision produced by the rod photosensory receptors on the surface of the retina, with processing of the rod hotopigment rhodopsin by Melanin in the retinal pigmented epithelium (RPE) See Drager, 1986

(Whole) Holy Black Body (H.B.B.)- See 1-33 TISSUE OF HORUS

Will-See Visualization

Women 's Moon Time-See Menses

BIBLIOGRAPHY

Akbar, N., Nile Valley Origins of the Science of the Mind, In Nile Valley Civilizations, Van Sertima (Ed.), 6 (2): 120-132, 1984

Andrews, Malachi, Color ME Right...Then Frame Me In Motion, Seymour-Smith Inc. 1989

Amen, N.A., The Ankh, African Origin of Electromagnetism, Nur Ankh Amen Co., P.O. Box 3191, Jamaica, New York 11431, 28-30, 1993

American Bible Society, The Holy Bible, Containing the Old and New Testaments, King James Version, 1611, New York, Rev. 1-22, 247- 263, 1982 ibid., Gen. 32: 22-31

Ani, M., Yurugu, An African-Centered Critique of European Thought and Behavior, African World Press, Inc. Trenton, New Jersey, 469-471, 1994

Asante, M.E., Kemet, Afrocentricentricity and Knowledge, Africa World Press, Inc., P.O. Box 1892, Trenton, New Jersey 08607,1990

Ashanti, K. W ., The Ashanti Brainwashing Test (AB1), Tone Books Inc., 5119 Lansdowne Dr., Durham, North Carolina 27712,1990

Ashanti, K. W ., Psychotechnology of Brainwashing, Africentric Passage, 5119 Lansdowne Dr., Durham, North Carolina 27712,1990

Ashanti, K.W., Rootwork & Voodoo in Mental Health, Tone Books, Inc., 5119 Lansdowne Dr., Durham, North Carolina 27712,1993

Assagioli, R., Psychosynthesis, A Manual of Principles and Techniques, The Viking Press, New York, 16-20,1965

Attias, J., Auditory-Evoked Potential Correlates of Susceptibility to Noise-Induced Hearing Loss, Audiology, 24: 159-156, 1985

Bailey, A. A., A Treatise on Cosmic Fire, V. I and II, Lucis Publishing Company, New York, 1925

Baker, D., Esoteric Anatomy, Little Elephant, Essendon, Herts, England

Baker. D.. The Opening of the Third Eye. Little Elephant. Essendon. Herts. England. 1977

Barr, F., Melanin: The Organizing Molecule, Medical Hypothesis, 11: 1-140, 1983

Barbeau, A., Comparative Behavioral Biochemical and Pigmentary Effects of MPTP, MPP+- and Paraquat in Rana Pipiens, Life Sci. 37: 1529-1538,1985

Barbeau, A., Environmental and Genetic Factors in the Etiology of Parkinson's Disease, Adv. Neurol., 45: 299-306, 1986

Barnes, Carol, Private Communication, 1992

Barnes, Carol, Melanin: The Chemical Key To Black Greatness, The Harmful Effects of Toxic Drugs on Melanin Centers Within the Black Human, Carol Barnes, P.O. Box 300918, Houston, Texas, 77230-0918, 1988

Barnes, Carol, Jazzy Melanin, Carol Barnes, P.O. Box 300918, Houston, Texas 77230-0918, 1993

Barrenas, M. The Influence of Inner Ear Melanin on Susceptibility to TTS in Humans, Scan. Audiol. 19: 97-102,1990s

Bayley, H., The Lost Language of Symbolism, Rowman and

Littlefield, Totowa, New Jersey, 196-231, 1968

Bazelon, M. Studies on Neuromelanin I. A Melanin System in the Human Adult Brainstern, Neurology 17: 512-519,1967

Bell, N.H., Vitamin O-Endocrine System, J. Clin. Invest. 76:

ben-Jochannan, "Y.A.A., Black Man of the Nile and His Family, Black Classic Press, Baltimore, Maryland, 1981

ben-Jochannan, Y.A.A., The African origin of the Major Western Religions, Black Classic Press, Baltimore, Maryland, 214-215, 1970 ibid, 73-137

ben-Jochannan, Y.A.A., We: The Black Jews, Witness To The "White Jewish Race" Myth, Alkebulan Books and Education Materials Associates,209 West 125th Street, Suite 218, New York, New York 1-0027,1983

Boylan, P., Thoth the Hermes of Egypt, Ares Publishers Inc., Chicago, Illinois, 1979

Bradley, M., Chosen People From the Caucasus: Jewish Origins, Delusions, Deceptions and Historical Role in the Slave Trade, Genocide and Cultural Colonization, Third World Press, Chicago, 1992 1-6, 1985

Bradley, M. The Columbus Conspiracy, An Investigation In to the Secret History of Christopher Columbus, A & B Books Publishers, New York. 43-54,221-228, 1992

Breathnatch, A.S., Extra-Cutaneous Melanin, Pigment Cell Research, 238-249, 1988

Browder, T., The Browder File, Washinton, D.C., 1991

Brunson, J., Frat and Soror, The African Origin of Greek-Lettered

Organizations, A Cleage Group Publication, 89,1991

Brunson, J., Before the Unification, Predynastic Egypt, An African-Centric View, James E. Brunson, P.O. Box 0962, Oekalb, Illinois 60115-0962, 1992

Bryan, C.P. Ancient Egyptian Medicine, The Papyrus Ebers, Publishers Inc., Chicago, Illinois, 1974 , Arcs

Budge, E.A., (The Destruction of Mankind), Legends of the Gods, Egyptian Literature, Books on Egypt and Chaldea, V .32, Kegan Paul, Trench. Trubner & Co. Ltd., Broadway House, Carter Lane, E.C., London,1912

Budge. E.A., The Gods of the Egyptians, Dover Publications Inc., New York, V .1. 424-423, 1969

Budge, E.A., The Egyptian Book of the Dead, The Papyrus of Ani, Dover Publications, Inc. New York, 1967

Budge, E.A., Egyptian Magic, Dover Publications, Inc., New York, 20, 1971

Budge, E.A., A Hieroglyphic Vocabulary to the Book of the Dead, Dover Publications, Inc., New York, 1991

Budge, E.A., Osiris: The Egyptian Religion of Resurrection, University Books, Inc., 1961

Bulkey, D.H. , An Electromagnetic Theory of Life, Medical Hypothesis, 30: 281-285, 1989

Bunch, C.C., Race and Sex Variations in Auditory Acuity, 13: 423-434, 1931

Bynum, E.B., The Family Unconscious," An Invisible Bond", The Theosophical Publishing House, Wheaton Ill, 1984

Bynum, E.B., Families and the Interpretation of Dreams, Awakening the Intimate Web, Haworth Press, Inc., New York, 1993

Bynum, E.B., Transcending Psychoneurotic Disturbances: New Approaches in Psychospirituality and Personality Development, Haworth Press, Inc., New York, 1994

Carruthers, J.H., The Irritated Genie, An Essay on the Haitian Revolution, The Kemetic Institute, 700 E. Oakwood Blvd., Chicago, Illinois, 1985

Czerkas, S., Dinosaurs, A Global View, Mallard Press, An Imprint of BDD Promotional Book Company, Inc" 666 Fifth Avenue, New York, New York, 10103.112, 113,234-237, 1991

Cesarini, J ., Photo-Induced Events in the Human Melanocytic System: Photoaggression and Photoprotection, Pigment Cell Research, 1: 223- 233,19RR

Chissell, J.T., Pyramids of Power, An Ancient African Centered Approach to Optimal Health, Positive Perceptions Publications, Baltimore, Maryland,60,61,65 1993

Clark. J ,H" Christopher Columbus & the Afrikan Holocaust. Slavery & the Rise of European Capitalism, A & B Books. 149 Lawrence Street, Brooklyn. New York 11201.1992

Clark. J.H., African People in World History, Black Classic Press, P.O. Box 134144, Baltimore, Maryland 21203-3414,1993

Clemens, T .C. Increased Skin Pigment Reduces the Capacity of Skin to Synthesise Vitamin 03, Lancet 1: 74076, 1982

Cohn, S.H.M.. Comparative Skeletal Mass and Radial Bone Mineral Content in Black and White Women. Metab. Clin. Exp. 26: 171-178, 1977

Cope, F. W., Organic Superconductive Phenomena at Room Temperature, Some Magnetic Properties of Dyes and Graphite Interpreted as Manisfestations of Viscous Magnetic Flux Lattices and Small Superconductive Regions, Physiological Chemistry and Physics, 13: 99-100,1981

Creel, E., Visual System Anomalies in Human Ocular Albinos, Science, 201: 1253,1980

Crippa, P .R., A Band Model for Melanin Deduced from Optical Absorption and Photoconductivity Experiments, Biochem. Biophys. Acta. 538: 164,1978

Crosby, E.C., Correlative Anatomy of the Nervous System, The Mac. millan Company, New York, 1962

Csaba, G., Uptake of Radioactive Iodine by the Thyroid after Pinealectomy, Acta. bioi. Acad. Sci. Hung. 19 (1): 35-41,1968

Devreotes, P.N., Protein-Linked Signaling Pathways Control the Developmental Program of Dictyoselium, Neuron 12: 235-241, 1994

Drager, U .C., Albinism and Visual Pathways, The New England Journal of Medicine, 314 (25): 1636,1986

Eberle, A.N., Melanotropins, Karger, Basel, Switzerland, 1988

Emboden. W ., The Sacred Journey in Dynasic Egypt: Shamanistic T-rance in the Context of the Narcotic Water Lily and the Mandrake, J. of Psychoactive Drugs, 21 (1); 61-75, 1989

Erickson, C.A., From the Crest to the Periphery: Control of Pigment Cell Migration and Lineage Segregation, Pigment Cell Res. 6: 336-347,1993

Faulkner, R.O., The Ancient Egyptian Pyramid Texts, Aris & Phillips Ltd., Bolchazy-Carducci, 44 Lake Street, Oak Park, Illinois 60302, 1969

Faulkner, R.O., The Ancient Egyptian Coffin Texts, v. 1-111, Warminster, England. 1978

Fenichel, G.M., Studies on Neuromelanin II., Melanin in the Brainstem of Infants and Children, Neurology, 18: 817 -820, 1968

Finch, C.S., Echoes Of The Old Dark Land, Themes From African Eden, Kenti, Inc., P.O. Box 361003, Decatur, Georgia 30036-1003, 1991

Forrest, R. On the Phylogenetic Origin of REM Sleep, Proc. West. Pharmacol. Soc., 15: 184, 1972

Forrest, F .M., Evolutionary Role of Neuromelanin, Proc. West. Pharmacol. Soc. 18: 205, 1975

Hawley, G.G., The Condensed Chemical Dictionary, Ninth Edition, Van Nostrand Reinhold Company, New York, 1977

Hillard A.G., The Teachings of Ptahhotep, The Oldest Book in the World, Blackwood Press and Company, Inc., Atlanta, Georgia, 1987

Holick, M.F ., Regulation of Cutaneous Previtamin D Photosynthesis in Man: Skin Pigment is Not an Essential Regulator, Science 21 (6): 590- 593, 1981

Holmes, B., Medicine In Ancient Egypt, The Hieratic Material, Lancet. Clinic Press, Cincinnati, Ohio, 1914

Hood, J .0., The Influence of Eye Color Upon Temporary Threshold Shift, Audiology, 15: 449-464,1976

Howey, M.O., The Encircled Serpent, A Study of Serpent Symbolism in All Countries and Ages, Arthur Richmond Company, New York City, 1955

Ito, 5.,High-Performance Liquid Chromatography (HPLC) Analysis of E- and Pheomelanin in Melanogenesis Control, J. Invest. Dermatol. 100: 1665-1715, 1993

Jackson, J.G., Christianity Before Christ, American Atheist Press, Austin, Texas, 1, 1985

Jacobson, J.I.,"Exploring the Potential of Magneto-Crystallization of Genes and Associated Structures with Respect to Nerve Regeneration and Cancer", Intern.]. Neuroscience 64: 153-165,1992

James, G., Stolen Legacy, U.B & U. S. Comm. Sys., Inc., 27-40, 1988

Jung, C.G., Psychology and Alchemy, V. 12, The Collected Works of C.G. Jung, Bollingen Series XX, Princeton University Press, Princeton, New Jersey,389, 1974

Jung, C.G., The Archetypes of the Collective Unconscious, v. 9,1, The Collected Works of C.G. Jung, Bollingen Series XX, Princeton Univesity Press, Princeton, New Jersey, 1969

lung, C.G., Alchemical Studies, v. 13, The Collected Works of C.G. lung, Bollingen Series XX, Princeton University Press, Princeton, New lersey,168, 268n, 1979

Jung, C.G., Mysterium Conjunctionis, The Collected Works of C.G. Jung, Bollingen Series XX, Princeton University Press, Princeton, New Jersey ,44, 548,592, 6(X), 606,648, 1963

Karsai, L" Hearing in Ethnically Different Longshoreman, Audiology, 14: 238-243,1972

Karenga, M., The Book Of Coming Forth By Day, The Ethics of the Declaration of Innocence, University of Sankore Press, Los Angeles, California, 1990

Karenga, M. (Ed.), Reconstructing Kemetic Culture, Papers, Perspectives, Projects, Selected Papers of the Proceedings of the

Association For The Study Of Classical African Civilizations, Aswan, Egypt, 1987 (6227 A.F.E.), University of Sankore Press, Los Angeles, California, 1990

Kastin, *A.,* Melanin in the Rat Brain, Brain Res. Bull., 1: 567,1976

Kerenyi, C., Asklepios. Archetypal Image of the Physician's Existence, Bollingen Series LXV, V. 3, Pnatheon Books Inc., New York, 1959

King, L.M. (Ed.) African Philosophy: Assumptions & Paradigms for Research on Black Persons, The First Annual J. Alfred Cannon Research Series, Fanon Research & Development Center, Charles R. Drew Post- graduate Medical School, Department of Psychiatry Human Behavior, Los Angeles, Califomia,1976

King, R.D., Audiotapes 1-3, Black Dot, Parts I-IV, Pyramid Bookstore, Baltimore, Maryland, 1993

King, R.D., Audiotapes 1-3, Uraeus, Parts 1-IV, Baltimore, Maryland, 1993

Pyramid Bookstore,

King, R.D., Videotapes 1-3, Melanin, and the Pineal Gland, Public Lecture at the Know Bookstore, Durham, North Carolina, Pyramid Bookstore, Baltimore, Maryland, 1993

King, R.D., Videotape, Melanin and the Pineal Gland, Public Lecture at Medgar Eyers College, 30 Slides, Brooklyn, New York,1993

King, R.D., Videotape, Melanin and the Pineal Gland, 100 Slides, Long Beach, C31ifornia, 1989

King, R.D., Videotape, Melanin and the Eye of Hero, Interview of Richard D. King, M.D. by Listervelt Middleton on the Nile River in Aswan, Egypt and Luxor, Egypt. 1987

King, R.D., Uraeus, From Mental Slavery to Mastership, Parts I-IV, Uraeus, v. 1 N.1-4, Aquarian Spiritual Center, 1342, W. M.L. King Blvd., Los Angeles, California, 90037, 1978

King, R.D., Black Dot, Black Seed, Part I, Uraeus, V.2, N.1, Aquarian Spiritual Center, 1342 W. M.L. King Blvd., Los Angeles, California, 90037,1980

King, R.D., Black Light, The Face of Ra, Durham, North Carolina, 1993

King, R.D., Black Dot, The Archetype of Humanity, Part II, Uraeus, V .2, N.3, Aquarian Spiritual Center, 1342 W. M.L. King Blvd., Los Angeles, California, 90037, 1982

King, R.D., Black Dot, Part III, San Francisco, California, 1985

King, R.D., The African Origin of Biological Psychiatry, San Francisco, California. 1988, 10

King, R.D., The African Origin of Biological Psychiatry, formerly published by Seymor-Smith, Germantown, Tennessee, 1990, Now Published by U.B. and U.S. Communications, 912 Pembroke, Hampton, Virginia 23669, 1994

King, R.D., Select References to the Eye of Hem from the Pyramid Texts, Durham, North Carolina, 1990

King, R.D., Select References to the Eye of Hem from the Coffin Texts, Durham, North Carolina, 1991

King, R.D., The Pineal Gland, The Eye of Hero, The Pineal Gland, Recent Biomedical References Up to 1992, Durham, North Carolina, 1992

King, R.D., Kemetic Images of Light, Ancient Kemetic Symbolism and Mythology Related to Light, Durham, North Carolina, 1992

King, R.D., Melanin, Black Dot, Recent Biomedical References Up to 1993, Part IV, Durham, North Carolina, 1993

King, R.D., Black Symbolism of the Unconscious: Part I, Review of Black Symbolism in the Collected Works (V.I-20) of C.G. lung, 1,1993

King. R.D.. The Pineal Gland. Melanin. and Calcium: Pineal Gland Clacification in African Americans, A Review of 1,622 Cases, Submitted for Publication in the Journal of Pineal Research, 1994

Kiss, J.O., Endocrine Regulation of Blood Calcium Level II., Relationship between the Pineal Body and the Parathyroid, Acta. Medica. Academinae Scientiarum Hungaricae, Tomus 26 (4): 363-370,1969

Kitay, J.I., The Pineal, A Review of the Physiologic Literature, Harvard University Press, Cambridge, Massuchetts, 1954

KlX:h, W .H., Photoiniated DNA Damage by Melanogenic Intermediates in Vivo, Photochem. Photobiol. 44: 703-710,1986

Kono, R., Anomalous Absorption and Dispersion of Sound Waves in Diethylamine Melanin, J. Appl. Phys. 50: 1236,1980

Koestler, A., The Thirteenth Tribe, Random House, New York, 1976

Kuhn, A.B., Who Is This King Of Glory? , Academy Press, Elizabeth, New Jersey, 1944

Kuhn, A.B., Shadow Of The Third Century, Academy Press, Elizabeth, New Jersey, 1949

Liberman, J ., Light, Medicine of the Future, Bear & Company Publishing, Santa Fe, New Mexico, 132-134, 1991

Lindquist,N.G., Neuromelanin and Its Possible Protective and Destructive Properties, Pigment Cell Research, 1: 133-136,1987

Lacy, M., Neuromelanin: A Hypothetical Component of Bioelectric Mechanisms in Brain Function, Physiol. Chem. & Physics, 13: 319-324, 1981

Lacy, M., Phonon-Electron Coupling as a Possible Transducing Mechanism in Bioelectronic Processes Involving Neuromelanin, J. theor . Biol. 111: 201-204, 1984

Mann, D.M.A., The Effect of Aging on the Pigmented Nerve Cells of the Human Locus Coeruleus and Substantia Nigra, Acta. Neuropathol. (Berl.) 47: 93-97, 1979

Marsden, C.D., Brain Melanin. In: Pigments in Pathology, M. Wollman ed., Academic Press, New York, 395-420, 1969

Massey. G.. Ancient Egypt, The Light Of The World, V. 1 & 2, Samuel Weisner Inc., New York, 1973

McGinness, J.E., Melanin-Binding Drugs and Ultrasound Induced Cytotoxicity, Pigment Cell, 2: 316, 1976

M(.-Ginness, J.E., A New View of Pigmented Neurons, J. theor. Biol., 115: 475-476, 1985

Menon, I.A., A Comparative Study of the Physical and Chemical Properties of Melanins Isolated from Human Black and Red Hair, I. Invest. Dermatol. 80: 202-206, 1983

Mercier, J., Ethiopian Magic Scrolls, George Braziller, Inc., One Park Avenue, New York, New York 10016,1979

Metaphysical Bible Dictionary, Unity School of Christianity, Unity Village, Missouri, 1931

Meleski, J .W ., Oral Methosypsoralen Photochemotherapy for the Treatment of Psoriasis, J. Invest. Dermatol. 68: 328.335. 1977

Meyer zum Gottesberge, A.M., Physiology and Pathophysiology of Inner Ear Melanin, Pigment Cell Research. 1: 238-249, 1988

Mishima, Y. , Preface to the Proceedings of the 14th International Pigment Cell Conference, Kiobi, Japan, 1990, Pigment Cell Research Suppl. 2: XV, 1992

Moller, M., Fine Structure of the Pinealopetal Innervation of the Mammalian Pineal Gland, Microspy Research and Technique 21: 188-204, 1992

Muhammad, E., Message To The Blackman In America, U. B. & U. S. Communications Systems, Inc., 912 West Pembroke Ave., Hampton, Va. 23669, 133-134, 1965

Murphy, D.L., Effects of Antidepressant and Other Psychotropic Drugs on Melatonin Release and Pineal Gland Function, J. Neural. Transm. Suppl. 21: 291-309, 1986

Nicholson, R. A., The Mystics of Islam, Schocken Books, New York, 57-58, 1975

Newton, P ., Private Communication, Baltimore, Maryland, 1994

Nobles, W.W., Understanding The Black Family: A Guide For Scholarship and Research, A Black Family Institute Publication, P .0. Box 24739, Oakland, California 94623,1984

Nobles, W.W., Africanity and The Black Family, The Development of a Theoretical Model, A Black Family Institute Publication, P.O. Box 24739, Oakland, California 94623.1985

Nobles. W. W., African Psychology, Toward Its Reclamation & Revitalization. A Black Family Institute Publication, P.O. Box 24739, Oakland. California 94623, 1986 .

Nordlund, J.A., Pigment Cell Biology: An Historic.11 Review, The Journal of Investigative Dermatology, 92 (4), Supplement, 535-

605,1989

Ortonne, J ., Hair Melanin and Hair Color: Ultrastructural and Biochemical Aspects, J. Invest. Dermatol.l01: 82S-89S, 1993

Path, M.O., Phagocytosis of Light and Dark-Adapted Rod Outer Segments by Cultured Pigment Epithelium, Science, 203: 526, 1978

Pearse, A.G.E., The Cytochemical and Ultrastructure of Cells of the APUD Series and the Embryologic Physiologic Implications of the Concept, The Journal of Histochemistry and Cytochemistry, 17 (5): 303- 313,1969

Pearse, A.G.E.,Neuroendocrine Embryology and the APUD Concept, Clinical Endol, Tinology S, Supplement, 2335,1976

Pelham, W., Twenty-Four Hour Cycle of a Melatonin-Like Substance in the Plasma of Human Males, I. Clin. Endocrinol. Metab., 37: 341-344, 1973

Piankoff, A., The Shrines of Tutankhamen, Bollingen Series XL, Princeton University Press, 128-131,1977

Piankoff, A., The Tomb of Ramses VI, Bollingen Series XL-1, Pantheon Books, New York, 208,1954

Ibid. p. 37

Polybius, translated by Scott-Kilvert,I., Radice, B., The Rise of The Roman Empire, Penguin Books, 625 Madison Avenue, New York, New York 10022,1979

Ponce, C., Kabblah, An Intrl1duction and Illumination for the World Today, Straight Arrow Books, 625 Third Street, San Francisco, California 94107,134-142,1973

Powell. A.E.. The Astral Body, and Other Astral Phenomena, The Theosophical Publishing House, Wheaton, Illinois, 1987

Post. R.H.. Hearing Acuity Variation among Negroes and Whites. Eugen Quart. 11: 65-81.1964

Mantagna, W ., Black Skin, Structure and Function, Academic Press, New York, 1993

Pryse, J.M., Apocalypse Unsealed, [The Drama of Self Conquest], Health Research, Mokelumne Hill, California (Reprint of the Original 1910 Publication), 68,33-75,1965

Quay, W.B., Pineal Chemistry In Cellular and Physiological Mechanisms, Charles C. Thomas Publisher, 301-327 East l;twrence Avenue. Springfield, Illinois, 1974

Rasen, S., Presbyacusis Study of a Relatively Naise-Free Population in Sudan, Ann. Otal. Rhinal. Laryngal., 71: 727-743,1962

Reiter, R.J. The Pineal Gland, V. I-III, CRC Press In (Boca Raton, Florida 33431,1982 2000 Corporate Blvd., N.W

Royster, L.H., Reproductive Hearing Levels by Race and Sex in North Carolina Industry, J. Acoust Sac. Am. 68: 551-566, 1980

Sandyk, R., Relevance of the Habenular Complex to Neuropsychiatry: A Review and Hypothesis, Intern. I. Neuroscience,61: 189-219,1991

Santamarina, E., Melanin Pigmentation in Bovine Pineal Gland and Its Possible Correlation With Gonadal Function, Canad. J. Biochem. Physiol. 36: 227-335, 1958

Saraydarian, T., The Symphony of the Zodiac, Aquarian Educational Group, P .O. BOX 267, Sedona, Arizona 86336, 1980

Schouten, I. The Rod and Serpent of Asklepios, Symbol of Medicine, Elsevier Publishing Company, New York, 1967

Sichel, G., Biosynthesis and Function of Melanins in Hepatic Pigmentary System, Pigment Cell Research, 1: 250-258, 1988

Sizoneko, P.C., Neuroendocrine Changes Characteristic of Sexual Maturation, J. Neural Transm [Suppl] 21: 159-181,1986

Slominski, A., Melanocytes as "Sensory" and Regulatory Cells in the Epidermis, J. theor. Biol., 164: 103-120,1993

Spencer, P., The Egyptian Temple, A Lexicographical Study, Kegan Paul International, Boston,1984

Stevens, E.J ., Lights, Colors, Tones, and Natures's Finer Forces: Marvelous Discoveries, Basic and Active Principles, Functions of Electrons, Magnetons, Atoms, Cold-Lights, Odics, Auras and Radio, Health Research, P.O. Box 70, Mokelumne Hill, California 95245,1974

Strzelecka, T ., A Hypothetical Structure of Melanin and Its Relation to Biology, Physiol. Chem. Phys. 14: 233-237,1982

Tota, Y ., The Importance of the Color of the Iris on the Evaluation of Resistance to Auditory Fatigue, Rev. Otoneuroopthamol 42: 183-192, 1969

Thatachari, Y ., Structure of Melanins, Pigment Cell, 158, 1973

Ukodari, M., The Personal Ascension of the Five Senses, Uraeus 14,53,1978 (3): 10- 14, 53, 1978

Valerian, V., Matrix III, The Psychosocial, Chemical, Biological, and Electronic Manipulation of Human Consciousness, Leading Edge Research Group, P.O. Box 481-MU58, Yelm, Washington State, C.F. 98597 C.F.,I- 98, 310-320,1992

Vaughan, G.M., Human Melatonin in Physiologic and Diseased States: Neural Control of the Rhythm, J. Neural Transm. Suppl, 21:

199-215,1986

Vigh- Teichmann, I., Immunochemistry and Calcium Cytochemistry of the Mammalian Pineal Organ: A Comparison with Retina and Submmalian Pineal Organs, Microscopy Research and Technique 21: 227-241,1992

Vigh, B., Comparative Ultrastructure of Cerebrospinal Fluid Contacting Neurons and Pinealocytes, Cell Tiss. Res. 158: 409-424, 1975

Vigh, B., Special Dendritic and Axonal Endings Fonned by the Cerebospinal Fluid Contacing Neurons of the Spinal Cord, Cell Tiss. Res. 183: 541-552, 1977 Vigh-Teichmann, I., Comparison of the Pineal Complex and Cerebrospinal Fluid Contacting Neurons by Immunl1Cytochemical Anitrhodopsin Reaction, Z. mikrokanat. Forsch. Leipzig,94: 4(8) 623-640,1980

Waite, A.E., The Holy Kabbalah, A Study of the Secret Tradition in Israel as Unfolded by the Sons of the Doctrine for the Benefit and Consolidation of the Elect Dispersed Through the Lands and Ages of the Greater Exile, University Books, Inc., New Hyde Park, New York, VII-XVI, 41-45,

Wassermann. H.P ..Melanokinetics and the Biological Significance of Melanin. The British Journal of Dermatology. 82 (5): 530-534.1970

Welsing, F.C., The Cress Theory of Color Confrontation and Racism, White Supremacy). C.R. Publisher, Washington, D.C.,1970

Welsing. P.C., The Isis Papers: Keys to the Colors, Chicago, Third World Press, 1990

Williams, N.M., Bone Densities Differ Between Racial Groups. Masters Research Project, Teachers College, Columbia University, Dept. of Movement Sciences, Applied Physiology, 1990

Windsor, R.R., From Babylon To Timbuktu, A History of the Ancient Black Races Including the Black Hebrews, Exposition Press, Inc., 50 Jericho Turnpike, Jericho, New York 11753,1969

Windsor, R. R. Judea Trembles Under Rome, Windsor Golden Series, P. 0. Box 310393, Atlanta, GA 90331, 1994

Woodroffe, J., The Serpent Power, All India Press, Sri Aurobindo Ashram, Pondicherry-2, India, 1973

Young, A., The Reflexive Universe: Evolution of Consciousness, Robert Briggs Associates, Box 9, Mill Valley